Budongo

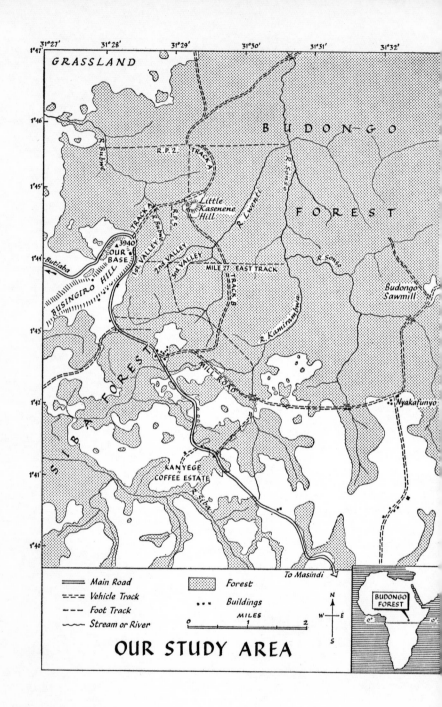

OUR STUDY AREA

BUDONGO

A forest and its chimpanzees

VERNON REYNOLDS

METHUEN & CO LTD
11 NEW FETTER LANE LONDON EC4

First published in Great Britain 1965
Copyright © 1965 by Vernon Reynolds
Printed in Great Britain by
Richard Clay (The Chaucer Press), Ltd
Bungay, Suffolk

To

FRANKIE

Acknowledgements

Many people helped to make our journey possible, and our stay in Uganda pleasant. I thank them all. I should also like to thank Captain C. R. S. Pitman, C.B.E., D.S.O., M.C., and Colyear Dawkins, for commenting on the manuscript, and David Kershaw for photographic help in Africa. I am indebted to Mrs Rosetta Baskerville for her collection of Uganda folk-stories. Most of the book was written in a little summer-house belonging to Dr and Mrs Ucko, and I thank them for the use of it. I also wish to thank members of the staff of the British Museum of Natural History who helped with identifications. Last, but not least, thanks to my wife for her helpful criticism.

Contents

Figures

Maps drawn by Neil Hyslop

Plates

The photographs in plates 2b and 3b are reproduced by courtesy of Ted Jones. All other photographs are by the author.

CHAPTER ONE

The Reconnaissance

We stepped off the plane at Entebbe with the whine of the jets in our ears. We had come four thousand miles in half a day. The contrasts around us on the airport were immense, but we were immune to contrasts. The clock showed noon by some African time; a hot African sun beat on the tarmac; black men of Africa walked around us; African elephants looked down at us from posters in the lobby, and as the plane taxied away and left us, a great silence, an immense inactivity was revealed all around, and we felt it rolling away on every side across that unknown land into whose centre we had plunged – Africa, and nothing but Africa for thousands of miles whichever way we looked.

Utterly staggering, when we thought of how long and terrible a task it was for Stanley, Baker, Speke, Livingstone to reach this very region. Their routes had differed from ours not only in that they travelled overland, but in that the only one who arrived here from the north, Baker, had followed the wandering Nile. The route my wife, Frankie, and I had just taken, straight as a die for two thousand miles across the eastern Sahara and over the Sudan, is still beyond the capabilities of man on foot.

We had woken at dawn. First a sharp red line had signalled the horizon, parting the sleeping land from the empty blackness of night. Then a red eye had blinked open, revealing a moonscape below: sand as far as the eye could see, stained yellow in the morning light, with here and there the long thin shadow, perfectly symmetrical, of a conical hill covered in blown sand. Looking down from our cool perch, progress seemed infinitesimal. Sometimes a range of hills, mountains maybe, casting enormous shadows, crept under us. Hour after hour no river wound its way below us, no path cut across the land, no cloud was in the sky. Then, twice, we crossed the winding dark ribbon of Mother Nile, drifting warm and lonely down below us. She disappeared in a blue haze, and all was desert again. Meantime

1

the sun turned from orange to yellow and the sand became white. We crept on, our Rolls-Royce jets mercifully keeping up their steady tune, rushing us through the icy upper air, incredibly slowly, over that burning desert. The shadows of the hills began to shorten.

The transition from sandy, stony desert to desert scrub was painful. The land began to darken and was peppercorned with thorn bushes, then turned into desert again. Dry watercourses suddenly appeared like systems of veins, then disappeared. Yet we finally reached the dry grasslands of the Sudan. I looked down upon the Nilotic tribesmen below, the Nuer and Shilluk and Dinka, whom I had studied from books in remote London years before, and thought of the photographs in those books, of their long-horned cattle and smoke-filled huts and tall, lean, heat-resistant bodies and naked skins. All I could see was tiny dots: huts. And I wondered idly why people lived in such a barren land, and wondered, too, whether they were standing down there with their hands cupped over squinting eyes, looking at the silver bird with its white vapour trail making a line across their sky. What did they think of us, those proud folk seven miles down below?

From grassy savannah to the richer savannah lands of the southern Sudan. Trees in abundance now, but rivers still dry. It is January, the height of the dry season, and fires are everywhere, glowing red and sending up pillars or walls of blackish smoke, turning the air beneath us into a dull purple haze. As we reach Uganda the lateritic earth turns red, the colour of Neolithic pots, and the land, as if in contrast, is green. We begin the descent. Roads are red lines between the fields of green. It is a promised land, it looks good. As we come down to a mere thousand feet we can see delightful red-roofed houses with flower-decked gardens, and with a simple upending of the wing we turn and see the entire world change to water below us, blue water on every side as far as the horizon, so much water we have to gasp at the quantity of it. Skimming across the surface of giant Lake Victoria, our wheels make contact with the clean white concrete runway and in big letters we read the magic word 'ENTEBBE'.

*

The ride from Entebbe airport to Kampala is by Volkswagen microbus. We gaze at the sights around us. We are not on one of those red roads we saw from the air, this one is tarmac, but on either side the grass-covered banks are of that same red soil. Every few hundred yards a great termite mound rises up. Through gaps in the roadside we see native huts flash by, with gaily dressed women sitting in front of them. Africans, the men in shirts and shorts, the women in dresses, both sexes with hair cut short, walk up and down the roadside. A few cycle. Around the huts stand groves of banana trees, their broad leaves shaking in the wind, and behind these are fields of maize. Every now and then there are brick or stone houses with tin roofs. And the whole scene, even the inside of our car, is enveloped in damp, humid air, reminiscent of the big glass hothouse at Kew Gardens. People move slowly, their teeth flashing in laughter as we go by. Here is a life such as we have never known, a concept of living totally different from our northern one, with its severity and speed, in keeping with the steady hot climate of this summer land which knows no spring, no autumn, and no winter. Topping a hill, we see before us the white clock tower at the entrance to Kampala, the vari-coloured buildings beyond, the gleaming domes of white mosques, and the red-brick Protestant cathedral atop its hill. Kampala is built, as Rome was, on seven hills; its population of forty-seven thousand is half African and one-third Indian, with some three thousand whites. Indians are everywhere as we pass through the streets; they run the shops and open-air bazaars. Indians are the mainstay of Uganda's commerce. Green bananas in great bunches lie around us, tomatoes and avocados, dried beans, dried fish, oranges, fruit of all sorts; the street is full of bicycles and people picking their way past each other; there are hundreds of cars and a parking problem. We glimpse sellers of tin kettles and coffee in small yellow bags, of jerry cans and tin funnels; smart clothes shops and stationers line the main street which we cross, going uphill past a modern Post Office to a big hotel, where our bus stops and deposits us and our luggage on the main steps. This is it: the beginning. We do not know a soul in all Africa. Has our crate arrived? Where is the university? How does one find a taxi? Are there any taxis? Who speaks English? In front of us, watching with amusement, sit three men under a tree with a huge collection of drums, stools, ivory, ebony statues, and birds carved from horns. Do they speak English? Probably not. And my camera is in the sun: the film will melt. Look at that cloth that woman's wearing! Are those vultures on that tree? A legless beggar holds out his hand – I have only English money.

Slowly, our minds clear; we order a taxi in the hotel; it takes us the mile or so to Makerere college; on our left is a tree-lined gulley and every tree is filled with twittering bats, hanging in huge clusters like dead leaves. The driver charges me ten shillings, which is five times too much. We enter a room, led by a charming African in a long green gown like a nightshirt and put down our bags. The place is ours, the windows covered in gauze. It is cool. The journey is over. There is nothing to do but sleep.

*

Frankie and I had come to Africa to study chimpanzees. This was the outcome of a long series of decisions plus a good deal of luck, determination, and hard work. And behind all that lay our interests – mine in anthropology, Frankie's in animal behaviour. We had both been undergraduates at London University, though not at the same time, and had both decided to do research, Frankie on rats, I on monkeys. We met, and got married, and planned this Africa project together, submitting it to the University as a worthwhile topic for research, since almost nothing was known about the behaviour of chimpanzees in their natural home – the African rainforest. Because chimpanzees are so closely related to man, it seemed to us important that an attempt should be made to find out something about this ape. We were fortunate enough to be given a grant covering our basic expenses. Now all we feared was that we should be unable to find any chimps. To know the answer we had to go to those very rainforests and start searching.

Kampala was having its January heatwave. While still in England we had bought a Land-Rover from a zoologist leaving Uganda, and on our first day we went to the garage in Makerere College where it was parked. With pleasure I saw that it was a very sound vehicle and worth the £200 I had paid. A 1956 model, in good shape. All it needed was the hood re-covering on top, and a new plastic back window; the present one had become opaque from the ingrained red dust of up-country Uganda: a foretaste of things to come.

With our Land-Rover we were mobile: Uganda was at our feet, or rather at our wheels. Dr Niels Bolwig, who was to have been our supervisor, on account of his great knowledge of and interest in primates, had unfortunately just left the Zoology Department of Makerere five days before we arrived. He had warned us that this might happen, but we had hoped to see him before he left. Undismayed, we followed his instructions and drove over to Entebbe to visit Dr A. J. Haddow, one of Uganda's finest naturalists, also a primate expert. He greeted us cheerfully and advised us to look at all of Uganda's forests before choosing a study location, but suggested that the Budongo Forest might be the best place to work. He then sent us over to Allan Brooks, Biologist to the Game Department, who was tremendously hospitable and shared Haddow's opinion regarding the Budongo Forest. This information was important, for, despite our efforts, we had been unable to gather any clear information in England concerning the whereabouts of large numbers of chimpanzees in Uganda. Now we were hearing from people who had actually seen them and had a wide knowledge of local conditions. We visited the Forest Department's headquarters at Entebbe, where Henry Osmaston supplied us with maps on which he marked the position of F.D. rest houses in each major forest, and gave us permission to use them. In addition he gave us names and addresses of Forest Officers to contact en route. Again, absolutely vital information. From John Blower, then Chief Game Warden for Uganda, we obtained on loan camp beds, a table, folding chairs, and a collapsible bath, plus a wealth of advice based on years of experience. Back in Kampala we collected our crate containing the motley collection of Government surplus and electrical goods we had sent out from England by sea three months before. They had travelled well: the tape recorder was still working, no camera lenses were broken; but we detected a faint bad smell around everything, and as we delved deeper it grew stronger. Finally, at the bottom, we found a nasty mess adhering to our tent: somehow a rat had got itself squashed inside the wooden crate and had, over the sticky hot months of travelling the high seas in a hold, imparted all the essence of its decaying flesh to our precious tent. The smell of death was strong, it had permeated through all the folds of the tent in a yellowish blotch. We tried airing it, washing the affected parts in Dettol, spraying it with Flit, but still the smell remained. Impossible to sleep in such a smell, but there it was; we gave up the struggle.

One of the most important jobs in Kampala was to find suitable containers for our gear. We settled on metal boxes in the end: rat-proof, water-proof, unlikely to break open, and cheap. We bought two big ones and two small ones, each a different colour, and each with a padlock. For the fragile equipment I required one further box which I had made to my specifications: it was of heavier metal than normal and very rigid, the inside was lined with foam plastic mats throughout and the top was not hinged but lifted straight off. A strip of rubber around the rim made it dust-proof and well-nigh airtight. It was double padlocked, everything of value went into it, and it served us excellently the whole time we were in Uganda.

Finally we bought a Tilley lamp, a jerrycan, and a score of other last-minute essentials, succeeded at the third attempt in getting everything into the back of the Land-Rover, and roped the load down. Exactly a week after our arrival we were setting off north-westwards on the start of our tour of Uganda's forests known or thought to contain chimpanzees. All of these forests lay along the western border with the Congo. Our aim in visiting them was to make a reconnaissance of each in turn; to decide which one would make the most suitable study area.

It was an odd feeling, setting off that first time into the bush. We had no guide, no interpreter, no experience, just a map with a number of crosses on it. Behind us lay London, the plane trip, our brief period of acclimatization in Uganda's capital. The months of preparation, lists of things needed, orders of priority, insurance policies, documents, tickets, the sheafs of correspondence – all were behind us at this moment. Every day for the past six months had been planned, now we had no clear destination and no time of arrival: we could take any road we chose. Yet this open space ahead was the final lap, all else counted for nothing in comparison. It was a fine moment, looking out towards the unknown as we rolled out of Kampala. Somewhere there ahead of us (it seemed incredible!) were chimpanzees.

Along the roadside women with concave backs hoed the soil, or walked serenely with loads of vegetables on their heads and, as often as not, a baby slung on their backs. Men rode bicycles, generally with huge loads strapped to the rear pannier – a big bunch of green bananas or a giant gourd containing beer. Bushfires blasted us. We stopped sometimes to watch insects fleeing before the flames – mantises crawling helplessly across the road to be taken by droves of swallows riding with the smoke. Children waved as we went by; for their pains we covered them in dust. We gave many lifts, all squashed in the front seat, mostly to Africans going a mile or two, but once to a white father, in a flowing robe of khaki drill, whose motor-cycle had broken down. He told us of the difficulties of making good Catholics of the remaining pagans in his area, and of syphilis – the widespread curse of the land.

From time to time we stopped to watch and photograph one of the big-billed pied kingfishers along the road on the telephone wires, always near water, looking like short-tempered brisk little businessmen with long cigars, or that handsome bird the long-crested hawk-eagle, or a tree thick with nesting marabou storks, a crowd of vultures in a field or a colony of weaver-birds fluttering and twittering around their pendant nests. Near Hoima, in Bunyoro, a baboon ran across the road ahead of us. We decided to stay at Hoima Rest House for the night. It was beautifully situated, overlooking a sweeping valley and distant hills. The calls of Africans came across the valley. A drum beat in a nearby school. Dust from the bush fires filled the lower part of the sky, turning it purple as the sun sank towards the hills. Our camp stove roared. We opened a first tin. Black boys and girls wandered along the road. A thrush-like bird sang. Distantly the crackle of the bush fires could be heard. We had escaped from civilization for the present at least; water had to be boiled; there were no fresh meat or vegetables to be had; mosquito nets hung idly above our beds. Night came and with it the shrilling of the cicadas. The Tilley lamp was lit. Small bats scrabbled in the roof and left, one after the other in a long stream. A sickle moon lay on its back above the balmy air. Life was full of promise and unknowns.

B

Next day, after speaking to David Lyon, the local Forest
Officer in Hoima, we covered the remaining distance to the
Budongo Forest. Here we made for the mill, where we met
George Barrow who was at the time Acting Manager. "Chimpanzees?" he said. "They kept us awake all last night, hooting
and shouting just behind our house. Must have been dozens of
them." It was as if he had handed us a nugget of gold. Looking
back on it, our excited inquiries and desperate attempts to pinpoint the exact spot on the map must have amazed him. Not that
madness is anything new among white men out in the bush, but
this 'chimp fever' must have been new to him. In order to steady
our nerves he kindly offered to put us up in one of the mill's
houses. We hadn't yet seen a chimp, but we felt keenly that we
were nearer than ever before.

Next day we set out to look for a man called Marco Okenyi,
the local Game Guard, who was to accompany us into the forest
on instructions from the Game Department, which were contained in a letter we had for him. His address was simply 'Nyakafunyo'. We found this on the map and set off confidently. Arrived
at the exact cross-roads marked as Nyakafunyo on the map, we
were a bit put out to find nothing but grass for miles on every
side, with the forest lying contentedly in the background. However, after wandering around for a bit we noticed a buffalo skull
and horns mounted on a piece of wood and vaguely remembered
that this was a Game Department sign. A slim path led back from
the skull, winding its way into the grass. We ventured down it.
After no more than ten yards we emerged into a clearing with
three huts, some women and dozens of children in it. The
children screamed. Both they and the women disappeared.

I tried one of the very few words of Swahili I then knew:
"Jambo!" meaning "Hullo". At first there was no reply. I then
enunciated the names "Marco Okenyi" and "Nyakafunyo". A
dog wandered across to sniff us. I put out my hand to stroke it as
a gesture of goodwill but it raced away in terror. So we just
decided to wait. It was the correct thing to do. In the bush,
waiting is often the best thing to do: it allows excitement to
die down and things can take their own course in an African
way. Before long an old woman, holding her dirty clothes about
her, came out and looked at us with great curiosity, but showing

neither anger nor fear. I smiled politely and mentioned Okenyi's name again. She replied in a soft voice, with no trace of effort, no movement or expression. Frankie tried to find some of the sounds she made in the Swahili–English dictionary but could not; perhaps she was speaking Lunyoro? I smiled and smiled as more women and children emerged. "English?" I said inquiringly, but none of them knew a word. They laughed and we laughed. It wasn't embarrassing so much as comic. The day was burning itself away, and we had no idea whether this was the correct place or not. Finally Frankie deciphered the word 'tembo' – 'elephant'. That made sense. Marco Okenyi was away hunting elephants. What time would he be back? 'Time' was 'saa' – we tried it and they answered "kumi na mbili" – twelve o'clock, which in our way of reckoning meant six p.m. With many thanks and waves we left them, fairly confident that we were on the right track.

In the evening we returned and met Okenyi, a tall, stately man with a broad smile and his top front teeth missing: we gave him the letter. As he read it, his wives looking on with awe, I noticed he was holding it upside down. He folded it up carefully, replaced it in the envelope, and handed it back to me. All the time he was smiling, and I thought what a friendly sort of chap he looked. Fishing inside my pocket, I took out a black and white photograph of a chimpanzee. He scrutinized it carefully, then called to a couple of young men who had been in the background until now. They began to talk about it and the word they used was 'soko-mutu' which we knew to mean chimpanzee.

Suddenly one of the young men, who was neatly dressed in a white shirt, long grey flannels and black shoes, said, "Are you searching for chimpanzees?" His English was almost perfect. It was as if we had been struck by lightning. From that moment on all was plain sailing. He read the letter, interpreted everything beautifully, and said he would come with us next day. We arranged to meet at seven a.m. to set out in search of chimpanzees. They had, it appeared, been heard by Okenyi that very day. The omens were good.

At dawn we set out. Okenyi was ready for us, and the two men, who came from a village called Dwoli, came along too. Okenyi carried his rifle. We drove a couple of miles into the forest along a logging track, parked the Land-Rover in the undergrowth, and set off along a foot track. We were in single file, the three Africans ahead of us. The morning seemed long and was chilly at first, but slowly shafts of sunlight reached the forest floor, more birds sang and more insects warmed to life. We walked a mile or so in silence, then sat down to listen. We scarcely knew what to listen for: we had read descriptions of the hooting and screaming of chimpanzees, and had heard them in zoos, but how would they sound in the forest, far away? Every now and then I heard a strange noise, but the Africans said no. They sat about smoking, relaxed. We began by listening tensely in anticipation, but slowly grew fidgety and bored as the morning drew on and our watches pointed to midday. Once one of the men whistled and pointed up the track: we saw a plump crested guinea-fowl, a beautiful dark blue-green bird with a red throat, the size of a chicken, standing upright and looking at us over the grass of the track. He began feeding, and two others stepped out of the forest to join him. In silence they made their way along the track, pecking every now and then, until they disappeared round a corner. We had brought some food and we ate it, the men ate nothing. They explained to us that the chimpanzees had moved away out of earshot and that it was useless to wait. We were disappointed, doubtful now whether it would be possible to find any. They said one could never be sure of finding them; we would return home now and try again tomorrow.

Half-way along the track Okenyi stopped and looked into the forest to our right. We followed suit. It was impossible to see anything. He continued looking and listening and we kept silent. Suddenly there was a piercing squeal, short and sharp, quite close to us, followed by a "de-dum . . . dum", as if someone had beaten a big drum. Something dashed off among the leaves. The Africans smiled back at us. "What was it?" I asked. "That was soko-mutu!"

To us the squeal could have been anything from a pig to an elephant, but the drumming was, of course, the moment we thought about it, typical chimp behaviour. Contact had been made! But how to study such a creature?

The following day we heard them loud and clear almost as soon as we stepped out of the Land-Rover. We were in the same spot as on the day before: they had returned. This time we headed off the track after a short distance, and had our first experience of walking through the forest proper. The tension mounted as we got nearer and nearer and their calls grew louder. We picked our way between the saplings, tripping occasionally to our infinite annoyance. Okenyi crept ahead of us, bent low; when we made a noise he looked back, his face intense with the searching, and moving his fingers up and down gently he whispered, "poli, poli" – "slowly, slowly". Suddenly he stopped and pointed upwards and ahead. We could see nothing at all. I crept forward as he beckoned me. I followed the line of his arm. Still nothing. He took me by the shoulders and forced me into position. I desperately scanned the treetops. Then I saw. A big black hairy arm was plucking fruits and stuffing them into a broad pink mouth. Farther back were others: we could hear them snapping branches. From time to time they called and the din was terrific. We edged forward to see better. One saw us and suddenly the whole area was filled with a different cry, harsher and shriller, there were chimpanzees everywhere, swinging about in the treetops, crashing from branch to branch, diving down into the undergrowth and rushing off. I guessed we had seen ten at least, but I had been too impressed with their tremendous size and agility to count them accurately. As they ran off we heard them calling. We began to talk out loud again, laughing and joking as the enormous tension in us found release. As we talked, a fine rain seemed to be falling on us. We looked up and there, superbly placed dead above us, was a big adult male, placidly peeing on us and looking down. We moved out of his way before heavier bombardment followed. Then I settled down with binoculars in a comfortable crotch, and with Frankie making notes as I spoke, began a long and full description of him. Every now and then he moved to pick some fruits, or he watched us, or he looked out over the trees to where the others were now calling. He was a fine male, with a balding head and greying rump, but not old, as his powerful, lithe movements showed. Later, we were to discover that a big male frequently stays behind, all alone, after the group he is with has fled. This one seemed completely fearless. We watched him until our eyes grew tired and our stomachs contracted with hunger. Then we left him there, walking away as silently as we had come.

On our way home we were in real high spirits; for the first time we felt it might definitely be possible, by concealment and stealthy approach, to make a chimpanzee study here. Our mistake today had been to give ourselves away: we should have been less eager to see everything. We reached the track and were just crossing a stream when there was a crash in the trees and we saw a flash of a big creature leap to the ground, then it was gone. It was a leopard, which had perhaps been waiting for a duiker – a small forest antelope – to come to the water. We were glad of Okenyi's rifle and remembered with a shock that he would not be with us if we returned here to do a long-term study; he had his own work to do.

That afternoon we all went to a local 'duka' (general store) and celebrated over bottled beer, European variety. The man who spoke English was a carpenter, he said, now unfortunately out of work. He asked us to try and find him a job and we promised to try. His friend was a roof-mender, also out of work. We promised to try for him too. Okenyi alone was one of those few fortunates with a job, and a good one too; but it was evident to us that he was a hand-picked man, an Acholi by tribe, a natural hunter and tracker. Significant that these qualities had got him further than education would have done. At dusk we went our several ways after exchanging addresses. The Dwoli men offered to help us if we ever needed help. We went to bed happy and exhausted, with the sound of the tree hyraxes in our ears. Next day we would head south to reconnoitre our second forest, the Bugoma.

We set off early, to cover as much ground as possible before the day hotted up. A chill mist lay over the gently undulating country as we drove along. Here and there the land was blackened where a bush fire had raged; rivers were dry; the red lateritic soil was baked hard under our wheels. We passed numerous small villages. Sometimes a woman was sweeping the earth in front of her hut and stood up to watch us go by. Between these settlements Uganda's countryside was pleasantly varied, with the road winding between hills which were dotted with low trees, and a total absence of hedges or fences, the land here being mostly unused and unowned. As the mist cleared we stopped at a 'duka' for a breakfast of bananas (fifty cents or sixpence for a bunch of twenty) which we had spotted hanging outside the door. By

midday we reached the forest and were heading up the Bugoma
Sawmills road towards the Forest Department Rest House
marked on our map. That road, incidentally, merits a word or two
as being one of the worst we ever came across in Uganda. Ruts
up to a foot deep went all along it from the timber lorries which
plied to and fro, and now in the dry season they were baked hard
as iron. The wheels of these lorries were wider apart than those
of the Land-Rover and so it was not possible to drive in the ruts.
Nor was it possible to drive consistently to the left or right of
them, because of logs and stones and other obstacles. This meant
that every few minutes we had to 'cross the ruts' – a hair-raising
experience as the car assumed crazy angles and everything in the
back flew about. We were thankful for the four-wheel drive,
thankful for the thick metal girders of our chassis. No normal
vehicle could have survived the beating our Land-Rover took up
that five mile track. We suspected that it would be us, not the
vehicle, which broke up first.

Arrived at the Rest House, we finally located the custodian,
who settled us in politely. The place was fine, except for the water,
which was the remains of some ancient rain lying in a dirty
yellow puddle at the bottom of a tank. But this was the scarce
time for water, so we didn't complain. Frankie set to work
boiling it up for tea; it hardly needed any leaves. We asked the
man, who spoke a little English, to see if he could find someone
who would take us into the forest next day to look for chimps.
He said he would try. Finally, before leaving us, he smilingly
said we should close all the windows at night, for there was a
leopard which prowled round the house. In the middle of the
night I was forced to go outside for perfectly natural reasons and
it was a hair-raising experience.

The Bugoma differs from the Budongo in that the forest is
not all in a compact wedge, but consists largely of a collection
of hundreds of straggling forest strips known as gallery, or
riverine, forest. Between them are great stretches of elephant
grass, which, at the time of our visit, was tall because it had not
yet burnt down, as it would do shortly. Next morning our guide,
who was called Xavier and spoke English, arrived. We drove
along the road a little way, then, pointing to a faint irregularity
in the wall of grass, he indicated we should drive in. I hesitated

but he seemed confident, so, engaging a low gear, we went in. As I drove I could see nothing but the wall of yellow grasses falling like a wave in front of us. We were following an overgrown track, and occasionally for a few yards the grass was discernibly shorter, but there were times when I thought we were lost. He pointed to left or right, however, and seemed quite at his ease. Any hidden object, a log or a hole, would have given us a terrible jolt. We might even have bumped into a sleeping buffalo. Bits of the grass flew in through every crevice in the car, I watched with dismay as the wing mirror was wrenched off, and every now and then I got out to clear the debris off the bonnet. Suddenly, without warning, we reached forest and the grass ended abruptly. We jumped out and found we were still on the track, which cut clean between the trees.

After a while we heard chimpanzees, faintly, and set off in pursuit. Now the differences from Budongo made themselves felt – in this forest were millions of ants, little, black, biting tree-ants which fell on to us and bit until we smudged them out, and the undergrowth was thicker and more strewn with lianas: it was altogether inferior forest, we felt. But we had to press on. After an hour or more we were closing in on the calls; Xavier now said we should wait, and as we did so a group of chimpanzees hooted and drummed quite close to us. He insisted we should wait. We sat still, our eyes trying to pierce the bushy wall ahead. The calling grew louder; it was as if a music-hall audience, shrieking with delight, were coming straight for us. Suddenly it stopped, and there was a pause, followed by a rustle in the leaves ahead. Something moved, darkly between the leaves. A space that had been sunlight blackened suddenly and then was light again. We searched, feeling the eyes of the chimps gazing at us, but we were unable to see them – it was an eerie sensation and we held our breath. The silence seemed interminable; were the chimps still there? More and more we began to suspect they had melted away on spotting us, fading out noiselessly among the trees. Or were they still sitting there, ten yards away, watching curiously? Suddenly I saw a movement – a long black arm reached upwards out of a clump of bushes, grasped a sapling, pulled, and up popped the head and shoulders of a chimp – a young one, curious and bold. We looked at one another. He scratched. An ant bit me on the neck; I let it. Then there was a sound to the left, the young fellow leapt down and was gone, there was a crashing of leaves and a booming of drums and a single wild call, and the silence of the forest set in again, quite empty and different from that tense silence when we and the chimps had been gazing towards each other, we blindly, they with inquisitive black eyes.

We asked Xavier about the drumming sound and he explained, in broken English, that there is a special drummer chimp who carries the drum, but it is closely guarded so that humans will not see it, and the drummer always goes last. Additionally, he pointed out to us strange circular areas on the forest floor where the brown leaves had been flattened and not a sapling grew. Here it was, he said, that the chimps danced and drummed and shouted when they had their carnivals. We later discovered similar patches of apparently trodden-down soil in the Budongo Forest, when we returned to work there, usually in a circular area of about ten yards diameter. What they are remains uncertain: the sleeping places of elephants? Despite our extensive studies of chimpanzees in the ensuing months, we never saw a dance in such a glade.

We tried the Bugoma a few more times in different places, but without success. It wasn't a pleasant place to work: the canopy was not dense enough to make it really cool underneath and the ground was a constant tangle. Probably it did not support a very large chimpanzee population, for we never heard another call.

We decided to move on to the Kibale forest, near Fort Portal, farther south. Everywhere bush fires were raging. Now we were on the foothills of the Ruwenzori mountains, and when for a moment the smoke-filled dark air parted we could see distant blue peaks covered in snow. Impressive green fields surrounded us, fields covered in low bushes only a foot high – these were the tea plantations. Huge bright red exotic flowers hung from shrubs, swallows and rollers and bee-eaters swept through the air, and all through the heat of the day the great mountains lay like a shimmering wall to our west.

The Kibale Forest was more like the Budongo than the Bugoma: tall trees, continuous forest for miles with cool shade underneath. We saw a group of redtail monkeys which jerked their heads and squeaked as we went by, and suddenly our tracker, who was taciturn most of the time, pointed into a bush and we saw a mongoose, frozen on a branch in alert concentration. It leapt away. Later he showed us a chimpanzee nest, but although we spent three days wandering through the forest, at the northern and southern ends and in the middle, we only once heard chimpanzees and failed to find them.

We pressed on southwards, following the line of the mountains, our next halting point being Chapman's Farm, at the southern tip of the Ruwenzori range, where a road ran up into the mountains to a height of seven thousand feet. On our way we went through the Queen Elizabeth Park at its northern end, seeing buffalo, kob, waterbuck, wart hog, baboons, and elephants. We came out of the park plains again and started climbing, finally reaching a village called Kyarumba, where the road petered out. We were now among the Bakonjo tribe. The people clustered around us as we pulled up, and directed us to the village chief. He was dressed in a clean shirt and trousers and was seated in a chair, talking to two other men when we arrived. We were impressed by the dignity of his face and manner and talked to him with genuine respect. A boy of eighteen or so, named Richard, interpreted for us. The chief, who was not a Mukonjo himself but a Mutoro, gave his permission for us to put our tent up outside the beautifully woven wicker fence of his compound. Next day Richard would accompany us up the road, no longer used by cars, to Chapman's Farm and on up into the mountains to look for chimpanzees. He was doubtful whether we should find any.

As the excitement caused by our arrival died down, and the children and dogs and goats departed, we looked around us. Ahead a great valley fell away with mountains towering beyond. Above our heads a flock of weaver birds twittered at their nests. A green, red, and blue lizard watched us from a branch. We began to pump up our inflatable tent with our rickety car pump. Only two children were allowed to watch us; they were the chief's; the rest were hustled away. These two stood close, their eyes filled with wonder as we took out our pots and pans and paraffin stove. A heron winged its way across the silent air of the valley. Richard asked us if we needed anything, handing us a bowl of cool, fresh mountain water. Evening came and the air grew chill: we were high in the mountains and felt like kings.

At dawn the three of us set off for Chapman's Farm. Was it just a name, or was there really a farm and a Chapman? People had told us that there was, and yet the road was wholly overgrown. Turning a bend in the track, we saw a huge dilapidated structure of great poles covered in rough bamboo thatch, and instantly three big alsatians, chained to stakes, set up a violent barking at us. We stood still, uncertain what to do. As we waited, the figure of Captain Chapman appeared from the log house. Finding we were fellow countrymen he came forward to greet us. He was old and his clothes were shabby. He invited us inside.

As we surveyed his home we marvelled at the toughness of his spirit. He lived on chapatis (the round 'pancakes' which are the Indian equivalent of bread), and these he made from cassava flour. There were also oranges, bananas, the occasional chicken and cups and cups of tea made from tea-dust. His larder hung from the roof by a wire to stop the insects crawling in. The roof had been damaged by a terrible storm and needed repair. The floor was paved with flat stones – how had they got here? A number of ancient, tarnished copies of the *Tatler*, the *Sphere*, and the *Illustrated London News* lay on the table, and a letter, years old. He had come here, he told us, from the Far East, thirty years back. He had searched Africa for water, a stream strong enough to drive a wheel, and here he had found it. There was nothing but the stream when he arrived. He had built a mill to grind the cassava into flour. People had come for work, he had paid them wages and they had grown rich, building a village. Everything was due to him. Then cassava flour began to lose favour . . . He took us to the mill, where he still produced a bag or two of flour every now and then. Proudly, he took a handful of the pure white stuff and showed it to us: we murmured approvingly at its lovely texture for truly it was beautiful flour. But it was cassava and apparently no one wanted it. Now the local men were getting cheeky; talk of Independence was in the air. They wanted his mill and would drive him out of it. They would force him to pay taxes. They were stealing his property: all his spoons had gone. He would go to Brazil and start again. The dogs barked and looked vicious; he went and talked to them. "The 'watu' (Africans) don't get away with much these days," he said. "If I hadn't bought the dogs I should have nothing left now, they would have driven me out long ago."

At times he raged, at times he was wistful and envious of our youth, at times he was cheerful and hopeful of life in distant Brazil. He pressed us for information about Brazil, as we sat drinking his tea dust out of grimy cups that had long since lost their handles. What little he had, he gave us – a piece of cold chapati, a drink of pure orange juice squeezed from the fruits within minutes of picking.

In bygone days when he first arrived he strode up the mountains behind the house, but not for the past ten years. In those days, yes, he had seen chimpanzees up there in the forest, but not now. We would have to go far, he said, and the going would be tough. Still, he wished us luck and saw us off, and as we started off up the path we waved farewell to him, unable to analyse our feelings. His was the most isolated existence we had ever known.

The climb up to the forest – montane forest this, and the first we had seen – was at a steady angle of forty-five degrees, and as the morning grew hotter we grew steadily weaker. Richard bounced ahead with the fitness of a mountain goat and kept telling us it was not far, not far now, but the mountain kept its steady angle ahead of us. Some Bakonjo villagers from higher up met us on their way down – small, musty-smelling folk in dirty rags with huge baskets on their backs, supported by a thong around the forehead. The baskets were full of cassava roots going, perhaps, to Chapman's mill, but more likely to the market at Kyarumba where they would be bought for boiling and eating in the traditional manner, like potatoes. Some maize and bananas went past us too. On and on we clambered, blind to the great variety of wild flowers which covered the mountain, growing desperately tired and thirsty. Then the slope began to level out and we found ourselves on top of a ridge. Ahead of us was a valley, on the other side of which was a village, with vegetable gardens, and, above this village, the forest. We sat down and looked at it bleakly, across the valley. We should have to climb down five hundred feet or so and then all the way up again, and up a good deal further on the other side. Distantly we heard music coming from the village: it was a strange yodelling, wailing sound, rising and falling, eerie. "Why are they singing?" I asked Richard. "They are not singing," he said, "they are crying for the spirit of a man who has died."

We staggered to our feet and began the descent. On the way we met a man whom Richard asked about chimpanzees. He said they were there, above the village. At the bottom was a stream: we risked the water and drank, and stood in it until our feet were cold. Above us, as we climbed, the strange wailing cries of the mourners became louder. Each voice burst out loudly, the note becoming higher at first and then trailing away down an unfamiliar African scale. Finally we made the village, sweat pouring into our eyes. The wailing went on unabated, and was coming from a group of people sitting in front of a hut; just below them a man was standing in a half-made grave wielding a hoe, and the rhythmic note of his hoe striking the stony ground added to the strange rhythm of the mourning chant. Those not concerned with the mourning looked at us with enormous interest; few white people had been here since Chapman came up thirty years before. This remote village perched on the mountainside had always lived as it did now, renewing its mud-walled houses as need arose, re-thatching with banana leaves, making mats and baskets, tilling the soil always at an angle of forty-five degrees.

These were among the poorest people on earth, we realized, and they seemed content. But according to Richard the Bakonjo were not content, for their lowland neighbours, the Batoro, were oppressing them, extorting high taxes from them, and keeping them out of the jobs which existed down below in the towns. Indeed, we had been impressed with the difference in wealth and hygiene (judging by smell) between the two peoples: no sooner had we started to climb these hills than the white shirts and shorts of the lowlands disappeared, replaced by dull brown rags. The Bakonjo were now, said Richard, planning to revolt against their Toro overlords, they would rise to the last man, sweep down to the plains and kill the enemy. I wondered, as he spoke, how it would be possible to mobilize all these scattered hamlets in their remote fastnesses, felt doubtful about the success of such a revolution.

Above the village the path wound on for a short distance to the fields below the forest. A woman dressed in torn sacking told us that chimps had raided her maize field earlier in the morning and had retired to the forest. Our hopes were high and we crept on up that remorseless slope. We passed fields of yams, their green leaves poking out of the mounded soil, and fields of cassava which looks like a tall shrub above the ground, while some cassava roots which had been picked were left lying on a big stone to dry out white. Ahead, the last field of all, at the upper limit of cultivation, was a field of maize. A woman, naked above the waist, was working here and for ten cents we bought a few young cobs, which we ate voraciously, drinking down the milky fluid in them. We took some more and gave her fifty cents (sixpence) which was five times what she wanted – she had no idea how much the maize was worth to us, and was not so bold as to ask a high price. She then showed us some cobs which had been bitten into and then thrown down, about a dozen in all; this was what the chimpanzees had done, and it was clearly that very morning, for the maize was fresh. Leading off from the field towards the forest, Richard found their track. We followed it carefully, and soon found some very liquid faeces, which were nevertheless identifiably chimp. A little further on was the peel of a ripe wild banana and the big black stones from inside it. As we went on, we found more of these: the chimpanzees had breakfasted on fruit and cereals!

The trail was very clear and must have been often used. As we reached the edge of the forest we were climbing on all fours, the slope was almost vertical in places. Richard showed no fatigue and helped pull us up the vertical bits. Inside the forest it was cool. We went on painfully slowly for about an hour. There were nettles up here and we kept getting stung. Not a call from the chimps, but we found a small group of nests in the trees, beautifully sited, with a long view over the valley to the plains beyond. Finally we stopped, utterly exhausted. The chances of catching up with the chimpanzees seemed remote indeed, as we were making so much noise and moving so slowly. So we decided that Richard would go ahead to scout about while we recovered our strength. Half an hour later he returned having found nothing. We were disappointed, but relieved that the climb was over. Even chimpanzees, we were beginning to feel, weren't worth the effort we were putting into this goosechase.

We came down by a slightly less ferocious slope, using sticks, as the Bakonjo did, to prevent us slipping. I remember we passed through a small patch of dense *Podocarpus* trees, like giant yews, deliciously fragrant underneath, and cool. We now, for the first time, looked around us at the extraordinary variety of wild flowers, and took in the splendour of this Ruwenzori scenery. We had been up to eight or nine thousand feet: the chimpanzees clearly went up still higher, perhaps as far as the tree-limit at ten to eleven thousand feet, but probably not far beyond, as there would be no food. As for the sheer physical effort of climbing, they, with their powerful long arms, would have no difficulty. We reached the village again; the wailing continued. Two children ran past us with strange wicker frames stuck with leaves covering them from head to toe – a ritual connected with the mourning? Distantly across the valley a drum summoned with its regular beat. We went on down. It was nightfall when we arrived at Kyarumba.

Next day we got off to a lazy start, dragging our stiff aching limbs as we packed our gear back into the Land-Rover. We said our good-byes to those charming mountain folk and especially to Richard, for whom we promised to try and find a job. Our destination was Mweya Lodge, in the Queen Elizabeth Park, where we intended to stay the night and look around a bit at the wild game. Down out of the hills we rolled, and were soon on the level plateau of Uganda again. We crossed the Equator, passed Lake George, shimmering to our left in the distance, turned finally into the road to the Lodge, past the sign saying 'Elephants have right of way', photographed some of these noble beasts by the roadside, and finally reached Mweya at the Kazinga channel. For the past fifty miles now the land had been flat and barren and yellow – the quantities of game it supported amazed us. At the lodge the only accommodation available was too expensive for us; our grant was not designed for such contingencies. So, with dusk approaching and menacing black clouds in the sky, we made for a cheaper rest house at nearby Katwe, on Lake Edward.

Katwe turned out to be a big, ugly fishing village of tin huts, smelling horribly and teeming with people and litter, the first such place we had seen – doubtless a result of the flourishing fish industry which had brought crowds to live there. We drove through, hoping the rest house was a good way farther on and, just as it was growing ominously dark, a sandstorm blew up quite suddenly, filling our mouths with grit as we asked the way; luckily we found a rest house and arranged to spend the night there. We were not a moment too soon. As we stepped out of the car a few heavy raindrops splashed on to the bonnet, and in an instant the most colossal storm unleashed itself, thunder and lightning and thick heavy rain. Unfortunately this rest house was none too waterproof and we discovered a torrent of water pouring through the roof on to the beds we were to sleep in. We dragged them away. The wind was now terrific and seemed about to blow the house away; for a quarter of an hour it raged and then slowly, reluctantly, things returned to normal. It was dark by now and we could hear our voices; the clatter of water on the tin roof had stopped. We lit the Tilley lamp and made a makeshift supper. Everything was soaking wet, neither the Land-Rover nor the house had kept out the storm. There were puddles on the red tiled floor: we left them to soak away. Looking at our ruined beds we got out the sleeping bags and prepared for a damp night.

Next day we discovered we had come to the wrong rest house. The one to which we had been directed was up the road, situated on a promontory running out into the lake, with a glorious view over basking hippos and elephants, with pelicans and plovers and the scavenging marabous among them and a troop of vervet monkeys in the low trees. To this house (which had a splendid roof) we now moved.

All afternoon we listened to the snorts of the hippos basking down below us in the bay, and the wild cries of fish eagles came to our ears. A flock of pelicans flew gracefully overhead, and one of marabous. Elephants came to feed on the bushes by the water's edge among the pure white yellow-billed egrets, wading in up to their bellies for a cool-down. Wart-hogs, buffaloes, and waterbuck could all be seen through binoculars along the lakeside in the shimmering distance. And yet despite all this, Africa hung heavy and slow as she always does in the heat of the afternoon. The band of vervet monkeys with their olive bodies and black faces filed across the peninsula of open ground, going from their low trees to the water; some were mothers with young clinging below

1. Old male chimpanzee in the Kalinzu Forest.

2*a*. Okenyi (second from left), his friends, and Frankie.

2*b*. The author, with the Budongo Forest in the background.

them. As the sun went down, the hippos' grunting rose to a muffled roar and we several times ran to the window expecting to see one on the verandah, but they were always down at the edge of the lake below – closer to the land now than they had been, and less compactly grouped together.

As the light failed, we saw the first one raise his bulk out of the water and begin to walk with a certain dogmatism in his regular steps – left, right, left, like a clockwork toy, away from the water and inland along his path to the trees, where the vervets were now roosting, and beyond to the stubbly grass somewhere in the far distance. Night fell and a full moon lit the wondrous scene from our bedroom window, as hippo after giant hippo emerged from the lake and started his own particular trek along his own path, doubtless to his own feeding ground beyond. What was most amazing was that the parched plains, which at this time of year were dry and yellow, could support so large a hippo population: each beast must have had to travel miles in its search for forage.

*

Up before dawn next morning and at Mweya in time for the Kazinga ferry which leaves at seven forty-five a.m. On our way to Mweya we nearly have a nasty accident when a hippo, returning late to his watery daytime home, suddenly finds us approaching in our Land-Rover between himself and the lake. He makes a dash for the water and, just as we are about to collide, thinks better of it and swerves off alongside us. At Mweya we meet our game guard, name of Dario.

Crossing the Kazinga channel we see cormorants, pied kingfishers, and herons. On the far side we drive for half an hour across the plains of Queen Elizabeth Park, yellower than ever in the morning sunlight, until we reach trees and a lake of unbelievable loveliness, as one imagines all Africa to be, Lake Nyamisigeri, with a flock of pelicans on the far bank, crystal water, abundant trees overhanging the water's edge, and, reminiscent of Kipling's *Just-So Stories*, a hippo blowing bubbles in his broad aunt's ear.

On again, and midway through a grassy level plain we meet a lone man, walking with a musical instrument called 'lokemu' for

C

company. It is a small square box with pieces of metal of various lengths on top of it, and on it with his thumbs he patters out a delightful melody.

Three crowned cranes greet us at the Congo Road, we follow it, straight as a die and yellow as the dusty plains on either side. Amazing – we occasionally see huge herds of topi antelope up to a thousand strong standing and staring at us from a goodly distance as we beetle past with our trail of dust half a mile long; kob too, and waterbuck: what do they live on?

We pass by a limb of the Maramagambo Forest, in the Park, where chimpanzees are known to live, but this is not our objective; Dario motions us on. Finally we reach a Game Camp at the southern end of the Park where another guard joins us. We shall make for the forest along the Ishasha river, which marks the Congo boundary, twenty miles ahead, and there look for chimpanzees. Each man has a spear. As we see the forest to our right, the guard beckons me to leave the road and head for the trees; a half-mile or so of apparently level grassland separates us from the forest edge. Bump! In a twinkling we jolt to a halt, poised at a crazy angle downwards into the earth. Where all had been level dry plain, the front wheels are now bubbling downwards into a little patch of bright emerald coloured grass: a disguised and overgrown water hole. We are out in a moment with the aid of our four-wheel drive and a good push from the men. We know now how the topi survive, and we know how to avoid plunging into more holes, so we weave our way between potential emerald danger spots and finally arrive near the forest where we get out and walk.

Dario and his friend go first as we enter the cool green depths. He says the elephants here are "kali sana" – very wild, very cruel. And no sooner have we stepped inside the forest than the men stop dead still, poised and listening, then, beckoning to us they point, and there, between the leaves ahead of us, we see the head and ears and long white tusks of an elephant looking straight at us. Almost imperceptibly, as we watch, he fades away and is no longer there. How impressive he had been, much more a killer here in the forest, where his bulk is hidden and he can melt away, than out on the plains where he is visible a mile off.

We move along the river, finding two or three old buffalo

skulls, heavy and with giant horns still full of menace in this disembodied state. A colobus leaps away overhead. We see chimpanzee nests, old ones by the looks of it. A redtail monkey. Behind us the elephants shriek, fresh elephant dung lies on our path, and huge footprints can be seen in the mud at the water's edge where they have crossed this swirling, brown, muddy river, with its periodic tangles of fallen trees and lianas and dark brown rotting vegetation. A bird repeats its single piping note, another its cadence; a woodpecker cackles; leaves crackle underfoot. Our two rangers with their six-foot spears held at an angle march steadily ahead of us. Two herons drift over the river, looking about them as they follow its winding path away into the trees.

It is afternoon. Our stomachs, which have had nothing but an egg and a slice of bread to work on since five a.m. remind us that we have far to return. The guard's hunch was wrong; we have not heard a chimp all day. The men are disappointed but we require no explanations. Hungry and beginning to tire, we peg our way back to the Land-Rover waiting in the sun and begin the seventy-mile drive back to Mweya and Katwe.

*

The following morning we left Katwe to look at our last forest, the Kalinzu, a huge compact block of trees adjoining the Maramagambo to the north-east – a bigger forest than any other in Uganda. We saw it first from the road. As we left the endless level plains of the Park and crossed its eastern boundary, hills piled up abruptly, one above the other in a steep escarpment, and from the road, as we climbed, we glimpsed ridge upon ridge of forest-covered country to our right, as far as the eye could see. Unlike any other forest we had seen, the Kalinzu was nowhere level, but scarred throughout with valleys and intervening ridges. In this it resembled on a small scale the Impenetrable Forest, still farther south, which we were to visit on a later occasion.

But the Kalinzu was less inaccessible than it looked. With valuable *Parinari* as its dominant species of tree, a Sikh-run saw-mill flourished there, and to this we now made our way along an excellent road. At the mill we met the manager, a burly Sikh named Singh, of rather terrifying appearance, with a big black beard matching his Wellington boots, blue trousers, a white shirt and a red turban. He welcomed us with twinkling eyes and flashing teeth, listened attentively to our story, assured us the forest was full of chimpanzees, and asked if we would like to see his guns. We assured him yes, but stated firmly that we were against the killing of chimpanzees, at which he looked puzzled. So we began again the story of our quest. Whether he believed it or not, he burst out in a hearty laugh, at which we were extremely relieved, thumped us on our backs and promised to see to everything for us.

And he did; his generosity was enormous and embarrassing. At first he gave us an empty house, but then he decided to put us in his father's house, with his father, and nothing we could say would deter him. It was a lovely wooden house, but not as lovely as his own, which was an architectural marvel in expensive woods and glass, perched on a hilltop overlooking the mill, in the foreground, and the forest behind. We were invited there for supper, which was a delightful curry served by his wife almost on her knees and leaving the room immediately she had put it on the table. For amusement he dandled his young son, whom I called 'she' for over an hour on account of his pigtails – a living plaything, with big, darkly made-up eyes and a look of unbelievable innocence, like an angel. After supper we sat replete in comfortable armchairs while he told us of his son who was studying at the London School of Economics, and we told him all about London. He himself was intelligent, tough, and shrewd. We sipped our whiskies and looked out over the vast breathing forest under a topsy-turvy tropical full moon and, mid-way through the evening, the distant calling of chimpanzees floated to our ears. A good omen.

For breakfast in the old man's house we had curried potatoes and chapatis. With this we drank tea, which was mixed with milk and sugar *before* boiling. Then we set off to meet the tracker who had been laid on by the manager. He was not there. After waiting for half an hour we had two alternative courses of action – to go to the mill and ask for a replacement, or go into the forest, of which we had no map, alone. We feared that if we did the former, the man, who probably had not understood his instructions, would be in dire trouble from Mr Singh, so to avoid this we did the latter.

Taking careful bearings we set off into the trees, towards the spot where yesterday we had heard the chimps. The forest was pleasant enough to walk through; we descended a cross-cutting ridge on the far side of the level forest, crossed a river by a tree bridge and heard, not far away to our left, a group of chimpanzees calling. Taking a new bearing, we headed straight for the spot. Sometimes it was necessary to take a slightly circuitous route to keep on the high ground and not get into the valley, where the vegetation was denser and there was water. We paused on a log to listen. Ahead of us the trees moved: we seemed to have stumbled right on them. Stealthily we moved a little closer, and saw a big black shadow in the saplings – it looked more like a gorilla than a chimpanzee. We waited. They had moved on a short way. We crept forwards again, but they were not to be seen. We kept edging forwards. Suddenly I was aware of two big forms in a tree just below us down the slope. They were chimpanzees all right, one was white with age all over the lower part of its back, and this one was being groomed by another big black one. They had not seen us, and we had a splendid view of them. To be on the safe side we hid in some long grass. Suddenly a young chimp climbed a small tree right beside me. We kept perfectly still as he went, watching out of the corners of our eyes. We could hear the pad, pad of his hands on the bark, and see the inquisitive searching look on his face as he gazed up into the branches looking for fruits. He didn't see us, but when he got to the top and settled down he did, and came tumbling out of the tree noisily. The others took no notice. There were more chimps about but we could not see them: they seemed to be feeding on the ground. We kept our binoculars trained on the two big ones. Slowly, the old grey-back got to its feet, walked away in leisurely fashion and descended the tree. The big black one turned to face us: he had until now been over-looking the valley. He sat there lazily, legs dangling, pulling in the odd fruit and eating it. It was only a question of time until he saw us, we felt, and we were right. The light may have glinted on our lenses; suddenly he sat upright, moving his head slightly to get a better view. He was a splendid male, big and tough. We waited; so did he. Meanwhile the others must have moved off, for there was no sign of them. We grew tired of waiting: he did not. We stood up, slowly; he stayed still, watching us. I was glad we had not come to kill him: it would have been a cinch. Instead I got out the camera and took his photograph. It was the first photograph of a wild chimp I had ever taken and one of the first ever taken of a chimp deep in its natural forest habitat. Amazingly, it remains to this day one of the finest, perhaps the finest I ever got (Plate 1).

Gently we turned our backs on him and walked away. At the last moment before we disappeared from sight of him, I turned round. He was still there, immobile, keenly watching us with his gruff, intelligent eyes.

Elated with our success, we set off on our return bearing. It was early afternoon. We rounded the ridge we had come along and crossed the river by our tree. We climbed the opposite side and then, inexplicably, found ahead of us another valley, which had no right to be there. The compass needle pointed us inexorably onwards, and yet I knew there was no second valley. We marked our position and cast about for some sign of our earlier track. Nothing. We thought of going back to our return starting point and tried to get back but could not find the way. We turned round again, determined to follow the compass bearing. Around us the trees now took on 'familiar' or 'unfamiliar' appearances. "I remember this tree!" I would call out confidently. "We've only got to go a bit farther this way and we'll see the road." There was never any road. We walked in circles. We did everything wrong. We got hot, angry, and desperate. Finally I got seriously alarmed, and Frankie began to cry. We still had not done the one and only correct thing in these circumstances – to follow the bearing accurately and absolutely, and this we now did. It plunged us deep into this valley we knew nothing of, we waded along its swampy bottom through shrubs which rose above our heads, frogs croaked around us and we felt that snakes were slithering away as we approached. Suddenly I had an idea: what if we had come in along a ridge, and on our return had followed our bearing a few yards too far to the left or right? We would then walk straight into a valley running beside the ridge along which we had come in. To test this idea I left Frankie

in the bog below and struck off up the right-hand valley side at
right angles to our bearing. The hunch was right; there was the
Land-Rover a hundred years away. "It's there! We've made it!"
I shouted to a grief-stricken Frankie below. And as if in answer, a
single low chimpanzee hoot came through the trees.

We stayed on another day, going in this time with the tracker,
who was called Sobiri, but we did not find our hairy friends
again, although we heard them. By now we were up to our ears in
curry. The hospitality of the Singh family was unbounded: we
scarcely had time to write up our notes in the evening before
someone was waiting to accompany us to the big house for dinner.
The father, we discovered, had a passion for religious wrestling
matches, and showed us booklets in English about the champions,
with photographs of huge-chested Sikhs in turban and pants,
and giving details of their appetites: one ate eighteen beef steaks
at a sitting, while another would consume a whole ox between
dawn and dusk. His own knowledge of English was rather small,
and his books were all in Hindustani. At night he sat glued to the
radio, an immense and costly piece of equipment, which made
sounds like a drain: this was apparently Radio India broadcasting
from Bombay.

The morning after the second day our time was up, and so we
left to return to Kampala. We hoped perhaps to come back for
another look at these fine Kalinzu chimpanzees. But in the event
we never did.

CHAPTER TWO

Budongo: the First Seasons

Twenty-seven miles from Masindi along the road to Butiaba, there is an S-bend as you follow around the bottom of a hill rising to the left; to the right is nothing but tall trees. At that point you are between Busingiro Hill and the Budongo Forest. At the beginning of the S-bend a track leads off left up the hill. Go up this track and on your right you will see a garden full of flowering shrubs and trees, white, red, yellow, and blue blossoms in glorious abundance. At the end of the track there are forty steps, and lizards, some with blue or orange heads, sit on them. These will scamper away into the dry leaves as you walk up the steps, or dash into crevices in the rocks after jerking their heads at you a few times. At the top of the steps you will see a beautiful white-painted bungalow, and when you reach its verandah and turn to look back, you will see a canopy of leaves stretching lazily away to the horizon.

That was how we first saw the house which was to be our home for the next eight months, for we had now settled on Budongo as the best forest for our study. Coming from London, we had not thought such a thing possible, and so we had brought with us a big tent, but neither of us had any doubts about the advantages of brick walls and a tin roof, even over the best canvas made by man. So that when David Lyon, the local Forest Officer at Hoima, had offered us the use of his Rest House for the period of our stay, on condition that we left room for visiting forest officers and other officials, for whose use it was intended, we jumped at the idea. And when we saw the house we jumped again, for joy.

Except for lizards the house was completely empty and, being made of brick with stone floors and plaster walls, it was pleasantly cool. To the right, as we approached the verandah, was a door leading to three big square rooms, each with glass windows and inner ones of insect mesh which we swung stiffly open; behind the second and third rooms was a bathroom with a washbasin

UGANDA'S CHIMPANZEES

- —·—·— International Boundary
- ∘ Town or Village
- ══════ Roads we took
- ▧ Forest known to contain chimpanzees
- ░ National Park
- ▲ Extinct Volcanoes

0 10 20 30 40 50 MILES

MURCHISON

NATIONAL

PARK

RABONGO FOREST

Victoria Nile

Albert Nile

Butiaba

BUDONGO FOREST

Busingiro

SIBA FOREST

Masindi

LAKE ALBERT

B U N Y O R O

Dwoli

Hoima

Lake Kyoga

BUGOMA FOREST

C O N G O

SEMLIKI FOREST

ITWARA FOREST

Fort Portal

KIBALE FOREST

RUWENZORI MTS.

RUWENZORI FOREST

U G A N D A

KAMPALA

Chapman's Farm

Kyarumba

Lake George

ENTEBBE

Equator

Katwe

Mweya

Kazinga Channel

QUEEN ELIZABETH NATIONAL PARK

LAKE EDWARD

Lake Nyamisigeri

KASYOHA FOREST

KALINZU FOREST

ISHASHA FOREST

MARAMAGAMBO FOREST

A N K O L E

Mbarara

L A K E

V I C T O R I A

K G E

IMPENETRABLE FOREST

Kisoro

Kabale

T A N G A N Y I K A

R W A N D A

Mt. Muhavura
Mt. Mgahinga
Mt. Sabinio

Figure 1.

and *bath*! Left of the verandah was a single room and behind it
a scullery and larder. Beside the house to the left was an out-
house, the kitchen, containing a large decrepit 'Dover' range,
while to the left a little way up the hill were the servants' quarters
in another building, and to the right was the lavatory or 'choo' –
a typical long-drop of the type found throughout East Africa,
with, like every other, its own particular insect fauna and dominant species. (At Bugoma this had been a long-legged hopper, at
Kalinzu a small winged insect on the walls, at Katwe a vivid red
cockroach; here it was a common buzzing fly.) Two tanks, fed
from the gutters around the corrugated iron roof, supplied the
house with water. One was of metal and stood at the corner of
the house nearest the kitchen, and the other was of stone and
stood at the other rear corner; the former was empty and the
latter nearly so, for this was still the dry season, which here lasts
from December to March. In later months these tanks flowed over
at each torrential downpour.

Behind, the hill rose up, covered with a tangle of dry elephant
grass and dispersed small trees. While Frankie set about
organizing the domestic side of things, I plunged off through the
grass towards the top of the hill. It was a nasty, hot journey and
the hill was higher than it had appeared; also the grass had burnt
near the summit and my clothes and hands and even face were
soon charcoal black. But the view from the top was worth it: the
outline of the forest's western rim was discernible, and beyond it
the escarpment with Lake Albert glittering down below and the
hills of the Congo rising misty and blue on the far side. A kestrel
hovered above me as I watched, and over the forest a pair of
vultures was wheeling, or perhaps they were eagles. A little wind
rustled in the leaves of the cork trees.

Down below again I was greeted by the clatter of pots and pans,
the roar of the paraffin cooker and the smell of a delicious stew
which Frankie had made out of our stock of tins. We discovered
an old lawn beside the house to the right, shaded by lovely
planted trees, and down below the garden was a ruined garage,
with roof intact but half its wooden walls missing, and, ludi-
crously, a termite heap two feet high in the middle of the floor.
We were to see that heap grow to four feet in the period of our
stay.

By evening we were settled in and felt it was home already. The last of the three rooms was designated our bedroom and living-room; the single room to the other side was to be our dining-room and the other two big rooms could be left empty. Having so little furniture (two camp beds, one table, and two chairs) we had no space problems. Once, faintly, we thought we heard chimpanzees in the forest below but could not be sure. A francolin rasped away below the house, bulbuls chirped like sparrows among the flowering trees. As night fell a ghostly bird looking like a nightjar flitted about and answered me as I imitated its call. Fireflies with their intermittent glow flew noiselessly through our garden. As we sat out, sipping beer, cicadas, stick insects, mantises and moths, came to our verandah, pulled in by the lure of the Tilley. The hyraxes began their piteous grating chant, like lost souls in the black forest below. It was all part of a pattern we would come to know very well: the pattern of living in the African bush.

*

Our objective was very clear: to observe as much as possible of the behaviour of our chimpanzees. What was a good deal less clear was how to set about it. There was no one to ask. Below us lay the shimmering green leaf-ocean of Budongo in which, somewhere among those one hundred and thirty-five square miles of trees, our quarry was to be found. No amount of waiting would help; we had to get into the forest and start searching. But, looking out from our cool, comfortable verandah, over the acres and acres of continuous canopy which lay dreaming before us as far as the horizon, we felt utterly inadequate even to begin the task. We were tempted to wait until we had found a tracker, someone who knew the forest well and, perhaps, knew where chimpanzees were to be found. But it might be a week or more before we discovered a good man, and, after all the delays and preparations, we wanted to make a start.

Even though we had got lost, briefly, in the Kalinzu, our technique there had been sound – we had simply made the mis-take of not adhering to our compass bearing. If we kept care-fully on course, there was no reason why we should not succeed

in seeing chimps here, even before we got a tracker. All we
needed was a burst of calls to direct us, and in the event we did
not have to wait long. Our second evening on the verandah we
heard the familiar howling and hooting in chorus from the forest
below. It drifted up to us tantalizingly, weak at first and then in
louder and louder bursts, while around us the evening grew silent
and still. The sound was intensely disturbing; in a strange way
we felt something in ourselves almost at bursting point, we
wanted to reply or to go down to the forest at once and join in
the *mêlée*. It was as though we were being left out of something
we wanted very much to join in – the feeling one has hearing
dance music or jazz calling one through a darkened Soho
doorway.

We took a bearing on the calls. Frankie cooked a camp supper
and we ate it to the music of the chimpanzees. Then, though too
excited to sleep much, we went to bed early.

It was still dark, no glow as yet from the eastern horizon
opposite our window, when the alarm rang. By torchlight we
dressed and Frankie groped her way to the kitchen to put on a
kettle for tea. Six o'clock saw the first faint streaks of orange
creep up beyond the forest horizon. The verandah was chilly as
we sipped our tea; the last hyraxes called from the gulf of blackness ahead, whose upper rim gleamed red like fire and showed up
the silhouettes of tiny distant trees against the sky. As soon as we
could see our way down the steps we got into the Land-Rover
and headed off down the bumpy path to the bottom of our hill,
then along to the left until we came to the beginning of a track
leading into the forest, which we followed towards the Bubwe
River. The previous evening we had calculated with ruler and
map that this would bring us close to the position from which
the calls were coming.

Going down the track we immediately entered the forest and
found ourselves in inky night again. A civet cat stood transfixed
in our headlights, its eyes like stars. We bumped along, making,
it seemed, a terrible noise, stopped at the river bridge, switched
off and listened. At first there was a silence, as if every creature
around had fled. Above the trees the sky showed, a faint dull
indigo. It was cold. Once something rustled in the leaves behind,
and an owl called. We were, in fact, too early: the day had not

yet begun down here inside the forest. It was fully half an hour before daylight penetrated to the forest floor, by which time we were cold and wondering whether we might have grossly miscalculated the chimps' position. So we drove half a mile farther down the track to its junction with another smaller one leading off to the right. As we got out of the vehicle we heard them instantly. The compass showed them to be almost due south. Parking the Land-Rover in the tangle at the track's edge, I grasped the 'panga' (long knife) and faced south, feeling confident that I could tackle this African jungle and its inhabitants.

Frankie, I think, was rather scared that first day as we pushed our way blindly through the giant trees, guided by the intermittent calls which continued to tantalize us. But she kept it to herself and, at all events, preferred to be with me down in the forest, rather than waiting behind and worrying at our home on the hill. In point of fact, I can say without lying that I was not scared on that first day, but it is equally true that this was largely due to false confidence. In the early days I did many risky things through plain ignorance rather than bravery. As time passed and we experienced more, talked to people with first-hand knowledge of the forest, and learnt from our tracker, I came to realize the dangers inherent in what we did, wandering unarmed through the forest. Frankie, on the other hand, took an almost opposite psychological course. She commenced our operation almost too scared to get out of the Land-Rover and was crying heartily before the first day was out, wanting me to carry a gun – even our little ·22 would have given her confidence. But as the days went by and we remained uneaten by leopards, unstampeded by elephants and unbitten by snakes, her calm and confidence grew.

We crept at first through long elephant grass at the side of the track, then entered the forest proper. To our left a sudden hoarse bark startled us. Frankie thought it was a leopard because she had heard that they coughed; I had other views but I kept quiet and looked at the trees. It came again, and I pinpointed the area and watched until something moved, and then I realized that our progress had aroused a sentinel baboon in the trees at the forest edge. He barked again, and again. So now the whole area knew it had intruders; the rasping repeated bark was like a burglar alarm we had set off, alerting every creature with ears to hear, spreading the news of our arrival. Too bad; we would rather have been unannounced. But the chimpanzees called again and we realized they might well be out of range of this baboon.

We pushed on, tracking south, myself cutting a path, Frankie close behind with compass in hand. We had made a vow that this time there was to be no manoeuvring and losing ourselves; it was to be straight in, and then straight out again. Every now and again our chimps called ahead, but never, it seemed, much nearer. My right arm started to ache from lack of panga-practice, and also simply because the panga was new and had not been sharpened to the fine sword-edge necessary to deal neatly and efficiently with the branches and creepers and thickets. Added to this was my sheer lack of skill with the knife, for, as I later learned from watching our tracker, every cut must be worked out momentarily beforehand, the strength of the blow necessary to do the job without wasted effort, and the angle of the knife to cut the branch diagonally through. I was hacking about and so I quickly got tired, and in addition my knuckles kept getting grazed and were soon bleeding merrily. Nor did our avowed aim of sticking to a bearing permit us the luxury, later taken for granted, of detouring round exceptionally dense thickets, so when great prickly hedges of shrub blocked the way ahead, I simply cut my hand to shreds making a hole big enough for us to crawl through.

But we went straight on along our bearing, too busy with scratches, twigs, and ants in our hair, fallen trees to crawl under or clamber across, and occasional gaps to squeeze through, to think about possible dangers. Every forest animal, bird, beast, and reptile, must have heard us coming that day.

And then came the first blow to our method – calls came to us through the trees and checking on the bearing we found they were ten degrees to the east of south. This could only mean that the chimps were moving. Moving away! Follow! Faster! We had been going for two hours now and were sweating profusely; without pausing, we pressed on along the new tack, hating the chimpanzees, cursing ourselves for the utter stupidity of abandoning civilization for this. And now that we had changed our course, something in us kept saying that every step was taking us farther into a mess we should never find our way out of; but

another, blinder force said to press on now, after such effort
already spent, and clinch it.

We clinched it all right. Gradually we closed in on the noise.
We moved in carefully at the finish, not using the panga but
creeping and crawling forwards, edging from behind one big tree
to another. A huge volley of hoots and hollers and howls and
barks shattered the silence just ahead of us, and the ground
shook with the noise of a deep bass drum – 'de-BOOM, de-
BOOM BOOM BOOM'. The noise was tremendously exciting.
Ahead we saw branches shaking, and then we saw chimps, two or
three youngsters playing together above, and we heard others
snapping branches as they fed nearby, and saw an adult female
who swung into full view before disappearing into the foliage
again. Observation was good, and Frankie was filling the pages of
our pocket book. Then I saw an adult looking back at me,
straight into my eyes. I merged imperceptibly with the tree trunk
we were crouching behind, kept hidden for a few moments, and
then ever so gently allowed one eye to peep out again. The chimp
was still looking straight down the lenses of my binoculars, lips
slightly apart, whole body tense and alert. I faded away into
the leaves for a full minute but it was no good; others had
noticed the behaviour of the first and were looking now to
see what the source of interest was. We kept carefully hidden
and waited, moving slightly to see round the other side of the
tree.

Here there were a number of chimps in another tree, who had
as yet no idea of our presence. At first I tried simply to count
them and whisper to Frankie, whose pencil was poised for action,
the sex and approximate size of each animal But they kept moving
and disappearing into the leaves, making this extremely difficult.
One or two were sitting still or feeding – an old grey-backed male
was facing away from us, sitting on a branch and doing nothing.
On a branch beyond I could see an adult lying stretched out
lazily on his back, one arm grasping the branch above, while
another chimp sat upright, industriously grooming his head.
Farther to the left I spotted something pink through my binoculars – it was a female 'on heat', with a great glowing behind. I
focussed on her carefully. She moved a little way, pointed her
behind towards another chimp – a male – and looked back at

him. There was movement through the leaves, a huddle of chimp, and a squeal.

Then Frankie touched my arm urgently and said, "Look!" Close ahead in a sapling not ten yards away to our right was a young adult, clinging to the thin trunk with hands and feet, staring at us fixedly. In a strange way, his square-boned face was like that of an Iroquois brave, and it had the same menacing quality. At first he chewed leaves and then looked at us, chewed some more and looked again. Then, suddenly, he let out a harsh, shrill bark – a different sound altogether from the hoots and howls we were now used to. He began to swing the whole sapling from side to side, looking at us, then he leapt off it to the ground and immediately clambered up another even closer to us. And now the most amazing sight, one I shall never forget, appeared before us – so incredible that note-taking was inconceivable. Chimp after chimp after chimp climbed up the saplings all around us, and up in the trees above our heads more and more of them appeared. They barked and shrieked with harsh cries. They shook branches. They leapt about. The whole forest seemed alive with them. The chorus grew louder and louder. Frankie had blanched. I asked her if she felt all right, tried to comfort her by a show of calmness, but she could not hear me even though I shouted. The chimps meanwhile kept closing in, one hung from a hand to get a better look at us. Then, suddenly, there was a great crash just behind us. Swinging round, I saw a branch, big enough to knock out a man, settling on to the forest floor: a result of the wild leaping about in the tree-tops overhead.

At this point there was no doubt that Frankie wanted to beat a retreat. I, persuaded by reason, knowing there are no authentic reports of chimps attacking adult humans unprovoked, suppressed my emotions and watched carefully to see what would happen next. Drumming boomed close beside us but we could not see the drummer in the tangle of undergrowth. The shouting swelled again and I timed a chorus, which went on for six minutes continuously, lulled for ten seconds, then swelled again. But now even reason had to give place. Every moment the chimps were getting closer and more audacious – it was as if they were working themselves up into a frenzy and I really felt one of them might boldly strike at us if we stayed. A look at

3*a*. Manueri.

3*b*. The author, with Sally the house-snake, and Frankie, with Gogo.

4. Chimpanzee in a fig tree.

Frankie's tear-stained, imploring face settled it: we could find out more later on. For today we had had enough; and so, turning from the crowd of apes, we crept back the way we had come.

Those chimps had been angry with us, I think, very angry, with a kind of mob anger. We had provoked them by our impertinent curiosity and insistent presence. Their display was, however, tinged with the same curiosity that we felt towards them. For we had white faces, and white faces are not often seen deep in the forest. What were we? Perhaps the crowding chimps had been as eager to find out more about us, as they had been to drive us away from their feeding ground.

If the morning had been exhausting physically, and the midday period with the chimps mentally so, the afternoon was sheer hell. For with that stubborn blindness with which only a vast forest can stare you in the eye, the reverse bearing refused to lead us back to the forest edge. We hacked our way on for hour after hour, reasoning and cursing. At three o'clock we hit a trace going from west to east – temptingly it lured us with the promise of easy walking and we succumbed, thinking that it must surely lead to the track we had first driven along, which we knew ran to our west. The lovely trace ended, after half a mile, in a neat mound of earth with a stick in it. We tried retracing our steps but could not be sure how far we had come. I couldn't recognize anywhere although I kept searching for the white slash marks of the panga. So we just pushed north where we thought we might have been, knowing that eventually by going this way we must hit the smaller track at some point. We emerged at last; looking around, we found we were about a quarter of a mile too far to the east, nothing worse. It was hot outside the forest in the tall grass, and the menace of Africa lay all around us in the dull silence of the afternoon. But there was the friendly patched green canvas roof of the Land-Rover; we dragged ourselves into it and set off for home.

Bumping wearily homewards we made a resolution. The chimps could call; let them. We *must* find a tracker, a good one, someone to wield the panga, someone who might know ways and means of getting to the chimps faster than we could. Next day we inquired of the local forest ranger, who took us to a hut where we met Manueri.

*

Manueri is the name of our tracker. He is about forty, but there is no great certainty in it. He comes from the northern foothills of the Ruwenzori and is a Bwamba. He is roughly my height (five feet ten) and stout about the middle from much drinking. His arms and legs are steely-tough, his walk is determined, his clothes are rags. But above all else, Manueri has a huge, wild, gleaming, wicked smile.

He is tough; he argues with me about wages, he argues about the hours I want him to work, he compares his miserable ill-luck working for me with the good times he used to have in the Forest Department and at the Mill. He mentions bonuses, overtime. I pay neither, just a flat rate day in day out. He talks about Sundays as if they were holy to him, and I agree to pay him double, at which their holiness vanishes.

Manueri and I do not know from the start whether we will get along together. He needs the money and jobs at his age are normally unobtainable. I need a good tracker and he knows the forest from fourteen years of working in it and drinking illegal spirits in it. His is the low paunch of the drinker, not the high one of the gourmet. His stomach has never distended very far: he eats to keep alive and he lives to drink. From the start I like him, because of that smile. But between smiles he looks sour and unfriendly. He has the air of a man playing his cards very carefully, when the stakes are very high.

He smiles and throws his hands up and says he cannot, cannot work for so little money, it is ridiculous to expect him to. I explain the work is simple, he will get increases. I am wary at this stage of offering him more; anyway I can't afford it. Finally we shake hands, it is agreed. He asks me to wait while he gathers his possessions.

Manueri's possessions are as follows: one blanket, one mattress, and two cooking pans. Apart from these he owns the rags he wears (rag-shorts, rag-shirt, rag-jacket), a hut which is dirty, dark, and empty, and a field. Owning the field makes him sound rich but not so, everyone around here owns a field and most of the land is unowned. Land cannot be bought, the chief gives it to those who need it. Manueri goes into his field and uproots some cassava which he places in a dirty piece of sack – another possession. Then we walk with the bundle to the Land-Rover and start the drive to our house, where he will now live. Eight months later I shall be bringing him back to this same hut for the last time, and parting from him will be sad.

For I did not know it then, but I was to get to know Manueri very well. I was to spend the greater part of seven days each week walking with him in the forest, waiting for his arm to cut the path, following his vanishing form as it twisted along animal tracks I could scarcely see. I was to rely on the tattered sight of Manueri's shirt with its great holes, and his shorts falling apart at the seams, learn to respect his silence when he felt like it and to join in his joviality. His body smell was strong and was only out-matched by the smoke of his terrible cigarettes. The pad-pad of his soles on the ground ahead as we walked, always in single file, was immensely reassuring. When he pointed, it was worth looking as a rule. Certainly, we had our ups and downs and I lost patience with him every now and then, especially when he was drunk and failed to turn up for work; but for his part he bore with me very well – there were many times when he could have laughed at me for my ignorance, but he never did, he always tried to explain.

And he was an excellent interpreter when I had to talk to other people, for I came to understand his Swahili perfectly, using all the clues of his facial expressions and gestures as well as the words: I got to know the emotional content of what he was say-ing. This I could not do with other men, whose dialects were different or whose conception of Swahili was based on another mother tongue than Manueri's and was thus totally different. In these cases Manueri would come to the rescue and put things in phrases he knew I could understand; if he said it one way I knew I could answer jokingly, whereas if he said it another way I knew there was something serious at stake. This was a great help when we later employed several chimp spotters, who came to me every now and then with a variety of complaints. "Je nasema . . ." Manueri would always start: "That (man) says . . ." and so on. In the end we always hammered it out, whether it was a question of getting wet, or 'ov-time', or whatever.

Manueri had some strange ideas, and some very sensible ones. Among the strangest was the idea, fixed quite immutably in his mind, that Europeans (some of them, at any rate) actually eat

Africans. I ridiculed this but he just put tongue in cheek and said it was true, although nowadays there were very few cannibal whites left.[1] Far more sensible were his views on clothes. He bemoaned the passing of the barkcloth era. Every now and then, in the forest, he would point at a tree with his panga and say "Hi Nyakatoma"[2] – "this is a barkcloth tree." We would gaze at it with respect. For, as Manueri pointed out, when the people wore barkcloth they put on fresh, clean clothes as often as they needed them, whereas now that barkcloth was no longer prepared, they were forced to buy their 'shirtsi' and 'shortsi' with money they had not got, and so they walked around in dirty rags feeling ashamed. "You should return to using barkcloth," I argued, but he laughed and replied that it was women's work; he had left his wife and child behind in Bwamba fourteen years ago.

We always felt sorry that his family was split. He was such a likeable chap, but who knows what lay behind his decision to leave home and family, to travel and seek work? He said he would return one day when he had saved up enough for the bus fare, but so far he had not saved enough. I asked whether he expected to find his wife waiting for him and he said, "Yes". I suggested lightly that it was a long time and she might have found another man, and he said "Labda" ("perhaps"), saying the word entirely without conviction either way. We felt he ought to return home when his working days ended – that his old age would be miserable as a bachelor away from home, with no income – not enough money even to buy a bottle on a Saturday night. He said he would start saving.

But what use was saving for Manueri? He did save once, with the following results. We had paid him his wages one Saturday and he had gone off gleefully – to spend it all, we imagined, on a vast week-end binge. So we were not greatly surprised when he failed to show up on the Monday morning. He finally arrived in the evening, and I prepared the usual admonition and threats,

[1] We later discovered in John Beattie's book *Bunyoro* what could well be the origin of this idea. It seems that at the time of Speke and Grant's journey through Bunyoro, a hundred years ago, the Baganda, anxious to foment trouble between the Banyoro (their traditional enemies) and the Europeans, spread stories among them that the Europeans were cannibals and given to the most terrible deeds.

[2] *Ficus natalensis.*

but his story was different and – though he related it with a smile – tragic in the extreme.

"Saturday evening we drank – a very great amount of beer. I knocked into two bottles of 'warigi' (liquor) – my head was just floating away. I went to sleep. However, the men of the chief knew I had money left over from my wages. They came to my hut Sunday and took me away to prison in a Land-Rover. I was in prison all of Sunday. Today they returned with me to my house and I paid them my taxes from the money I had saved. I owed them poll tax for two years, the money was still not enough. I have lost all my wages and still I owe them money." And, as so often, his story ended with the plea, "Mimi nataka r'vance, bwana – shillingi tano tu" – "I need an advance, sir, only five shillings."

Of course he should have kept up his poll tax payments. Every man who owns a house has to pay poll tax to the local chief, everybody knows that. There is only one snag: it is an impossible sum for those who have no work. The chiefs use all sorts of means to obtain their dues, once they know a man has some money. For example, where wages are paid over a table, their henchmen stand around and pounce on men who owe them money the moment the wage-packet is handed over. To counteract this, men who owe tax pretend to be sick at pay-time and get their money later. Word must have got to the chief's men that Manueri had money saved up and so they had grabbed their man. Now his savings were gone and he had nothing again.

He accepted this disaster with a cheerful fatalism which we already knew in him. Manueri was too old to grieve. Life was, for him, a light-hearted battle of wits in which the most subtle and skilful man won. This was evident in all our arguments, which frequently centred around wages or hours of work: if he could prove his point in logical argument he expected (and got) his way, and if I convinced him on a technical point he conceded the battle cheerfully enough. Hidden malice and the sulks were qualities he lacked entirely.

He was a hard man to surprise and I can only remember one occasion when he was absolutely thunderstruck. All of one day we had been close to a large group of chimpanzees, tape-recording their wild choruses. He had watched my antics with the Grampian

microphone as I stuck it at a suitable angle in a branch; he had
seen the magic eye of the machine flicker as the sound of the
chimps rose to a crescendo; he had seen me twiddling knobs and
had spent the whole day in enforced silence, seeing me frown
and put a finger to my lips whenever he coughed his awful,
chesty smoker's cough. He must have wondered what it was all
about.

When we got back home that evening we waited until after
supper when the hill was all in darkness and then, placing the
tape recorder in the middle of the lawn, I switched it on at
maximum volume and retired to our table to await results. In
no time the night air was filled with screams and hoots, as if a
great tribe of apes was sweeping up the hill. Frankie and I sat
nonchalantly sipping beer. In a minute a hesitant form appeared,
knife in hand, mouth agape.

"Wapi soko-mutu?" – "Where are the chimps?" asked
Manueri.

"Chimps? What chimps? Asleep in the forest, I suppose."

"Can't you hear chimps?"

"*Hear* chimps? – No – you must be drunk."

"I'm not drunk."

But we couldn't keep it up, and it was grossly unfair. When
he saw that our magic box was making all that chimp noise, he
just shook his head and laughed. He christened the tape-recorder
"soko-mutu ya nyumbani" – "chimps of the home"; and thereafter that was what we always called it.

*

With Manueri, chimp-watching took a new turn – for the
better. No more the bleeding knuckles and frayed tempers of
that awful first day. We now adjusted to the unhurried, silent,
thoughtful way in which a skilled man makes his way through the
forest, looking always a little to left and right of the true path
for any signs of space in the tangle ahead, even stopping occasionally and thrusting down the panga as a marker, before moving to
the left and then the right in search of a clear way through.
When this had been found, a minimum of essential cutting
usually got us across the most baffling array of forestry.

Our methods on finally approaching the chimpanzees became more cautious. At first, as on the first day, they got excited when they saw us. We had hopes that they might grow accustomed to our presence and, seeing that we did no harm, learn to ignore us. But in the event, unfortunately, just the opposite happened – more and more often, as the days went by, the response of chimps on spotting us was that they all quickly descended the trees, usually in silence, and made off deep into the forest along their own network of tracks which criss-crossed the undergrowth of the forest floor. Then we would have to sit down and waste a lot of time, listening for their next calls, which might be a mile or more off when they came.

The reasons, most probably, why we failed to habituate the chimps to our presence were as follows. For a start, there were always the three of us, and three people are quite obviously more frightening than one would have been. Secondly, in dense forest the chimpanzees must often have failed to see us distinctly at all, especially as, high up in the sunshine on the forest roof, their eyes must have had difficulty in adjusting to the gloomy shadows of the forest floor. Any strange creatures wandering stealthily below would therefore seem all the more suspicious. But I believe both these reasons were less important than a third one – that we were seeing different chimps, or different combinations of chimps, on every occasion, so that in fact none of them had much chance to get to know us. Added to which, of course, humans are an extreme rarity inside the forest so that their presence is bound to arouse suspicion or fear in animals, and the more so if the animals feel they are being actively pursued, and stared at with keen interest.

We soon gave up altogether the attempt to habituate a group of chimps to our presence – they were too mobile, too volatile: finding them was so hard and losing them so easy. We decided we must observe them without their knowing. An easy decision – but one which we never in eight months succeeded fully in putting into effect. For though the chimpanzees never seemed to be disturbed by the sounds of our approach, we found we had to deal with uncanny eyesight.

Our binoculars were a problem. We had to use them, as we were generally observing the chimpanzees from about sixty or so

yards away. This distance, we found, combined several advantages. Farther away, too many branches and leaves intervened
and we simply could not see up into the treetops where the chimpanzees were. At sixty yards, the angle from our position to the
top canopy was such that, by finding gaps in the lower canopies
to peer through, we kept fairly well hidden and yet got a good,
sideways on, view of the chimps. Coming closer to them increased the danger that we would be seen, and meant that we
had to crane our necks into awkward angles in order to see
anything.

But although we hid as carefully as we could, our binocular
lenses must have glinted in shafts of light, and so the inevitable
happened, sooner or later – one suddenly had the awful knowledge that a chimp was looking straight back down one's binoculars into one's eyes, a stomach-turning reversal of the field-
worker's intentions. And then, with this knowledge, one just
had to edge fractionally to one side, behind the cover of tree or
bush, gently, and feign total non-existence for a few minutes,
hoping for the best. "Moja naona mimi," I would whisper to
Manueri on these tense occasions: "One has seen me," and we
would all wait with bated breath for any tell-tale signs of panic in
the trees ahead – worried moans, or shrill alarm barks, or the
noise of foliage shaking as a party of chimps made their get-
away, and perhaps the thud of feet as they jumped to the ground.

For this problem we found no solution: it was their wits
against ours. For days we tried perfecting our camouflage (for
our bodies were covered in jungle-coloured clothes) by covering
our heads and binoculars and hands all over in camouflage netting
as we got near the chimpanzees, but it was no use – the net over
the lenses made the chimps fuzzy and strained our eyes, and our
head-nets kept catching on overhanging spikes and twigs, causing
swearings and mutterings to break out on the forest floor and
general bad humour to overtake the party. Added to which the
nets were so effective that we kept losing each other, and had to
take them off before we could spot each other again.

But, imperceptibly, we were improving. Manueri was showing
us forest-lore and we were slowly cutting out inessentials and
noticing the important things – we were becoming 'of the forest'.
And one of our first major discoveries took place: wherever we

tracked down a party of chimps, we discovered them eating a juicy yellow fig, which Manueri called "Mukunyu" (later identified from our collected samples as *Ficus mucuso*). It was, for the chimps, the Mukunyu season.

This fruit was obviously a great favourite with them. Day after day we found large groups, fifteen or more chimpanzees, gathered on the fig trees, hooting and shouting loud and long as they stuffed great quantities of the figs into their mouths, chewed them up, two or three at a time, and swallowed them down into stomachs which already looked full to bursting, looking around the while for another nice little cluster with the pink blush of ripeness on the orange skins. After a few hours of fig-feasting their faeces were almost pure wads of indigestible fig-seeds and the smell under the tree, where millions of minute midges hummed over the débris, reminded one of nothing more than Paris *pissoirs*. During this fig season we got to know the location of a good many individual trees and the best approach to adopt in each case to avoid being seen, and the best place to watch from. We found that they were usually in sunny spots, often on the slope of a valley; and we came to admire these fine trees, which are extremely large and beautiful, for they possess an incredibly smooth sandy-brown bark contrasting nicely with the bright green of the leaves and the yellow fruits. We were as delighted as the chimps by the sight of a tree with "chakula *mingi* sana!" as Manueri put it, waving his hand downwards, wide-eyed, smiling – "*very* much food!" We grew used to settling down for several hours of continuous observation, identifying individuals as they moved about the tree, taking copious notes, tape-recording from close-to the incredible din of their voices. In short we were thoroughly spoilt, and when in late April the season ended, and one by one the remaining fig-trees gave up their bounty to the chimpanzees and were 'kwisha' – 'finished', not only were the chimps forced to change their tactics in order to find new sources of food, but we were left helpless and without any idea where to look.

During early May the shouting and the hooting, which had been our magnet and the essential signal we needed to pinpoint, get a compass bearing on, and track down our target, all this sound and fury which we had come to take for granted, died

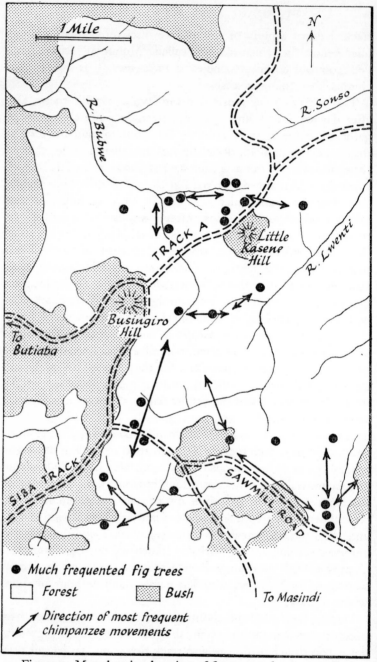

Figure 2. Map showing location of fig trees and corresponding movements of chimpanzees.

away to nothing. It was as if every chimpanzee had left the area. To test this idea we went far beyond our previous study area but to no avail. All was silent. Day after day we wandered in the forest, trying one area after another, hearing what seemed to be a weak call, following it as fast as we could, getting hot and tired and ill-tempered, before finally, after hearing no more and finding nothing, we gave up. Several ideas went through our heads during those frustrating days and weeks, the most worrying of which was that the chimps, having spotted us on a number of occasions and fled, were now afraid and by mutual agreement, passed from chimp to chimp along the jungle telegraph, were keeping silent until we moved away from the forest.

Then one day we happened to be near some chimps and heard a few calls – individuals calling, no great group choruses of the kind we were used to – and came upon the chimps. To our surprise they were not up in the trees but down in the saplings just ten or twenty feet from the ground, two or three chimpanzees, rapidly stuffing something into their mouths and then, with great skill, moving outwards in the top of the sapling, bending it over by their weight, and finally leaping off it on to a neighbouring sapling. We looked carefully to see what they were eating: it was leaves, the young tender leaves at the extremities of the branches. We found faeces, and they were green, almost entirely composed of leaves. I say 'almost' advisedly, for it has never been shown that chimpanzees can survive on a diet of leaves and nothing but leaves. From what we saw we could conclude no more than that the chimpanzees, for periods of the day, were eating leaves: they may have been supplementing this with insects, fruit or pith and we once saw them chewing wood. We now knew something of the conditions underlying the silence of the chimpanzees, which was as spectacular as their noisy outbursts had been, if more depressing.

As days went by we bumped into a few more groups, usually after painstaking tracking on a minimum of evidence, and found the same picture repeated time after time: small groups feeding voraciously on leaves as if they could never get enough, keeping quiet for most of the time. And in our wanderings we came to realize that there was no fruit on the trees, and none lying rotting under them: the figs had ended weeks ago and nothing had replaced them. Now the chimpanzees' behaviour made good sense: they had split up into little bands to forage all over the forest because there were no giant fruiting trees acting as focal points of attraction. And their silence could most simply be explained by the theory that leaves, in contrast to figs, were nothing to shout about.

Our idea that the chimps were keeping quiet because of our intrusion into the forest had been pure nonsense. We plodded on, day after day, sometimes drawing a blank, sometimes finding a little group. And then, like all things, the lean times came to an end. It was nothing to do with the weather, not a dry season ending or anything like that; in fact, the dry season had coincided with the fig season and now there had been plenty of rain but no fruits. But the day came, in late May, when we heard once again the hollering and hooting of the good old days and came upon a sizable group of chimpanzees in a small, rather gnarled under-storey tree eating yellow-orange fruits which looked like a sort of Siamese-twin-apricot, but, unfortunately for us, tasted bitter and astringent like nearly all chimpanzee foods. Again and again we found them on this species of tree which was now coming into fruit all over the forest; it was called 'Ngrube' (*Melanodiscus sp.*). Conditions for watching were not too good because, as it was an understorey tree, our visibility was more restricted than when the chimps were high up above in the canopy. But that didn't matter. At least we were finding them easily again. For they now began to express their excitement as crowds of ten or more gathered on a bountiful tree: whether it was the fruit or the com-pany that made them yell we did not know. The trees were scattered widely, unlike the fig trees which generally had been separated from each other by no more than half a mile or so along a valley, or along the edges of a forest trace. So when a tree was finished we generally lost the chimps and were unable to follow them to the next tree, as we had sometimes succeeded in doing in the fig season. And we realized that the excitement caused now by the Ngrube was less extreme than that caused by the figs: while a Mukunyu would produced a jamboree, the result of a ripe Ngrube was more like a vicarage garden party. We got our observations, however, and although at this time the animals tended to spot us and would then instantly flee, we were grateful for every small mercy after the emptiness of the weeks before.

Looking back on our first months of observation, we saw that we had witnessed three distinct periods in the chimpanzees' food cycle: the fig season, the lean season, and the Ngrube season. These 'seasons' were determined by the forces governing the forest: the inter-relations between its tree species, the utilization by each species of its own particular ecological niche, each playing its part in the overall pattern, each struggling to survive against the relentless opposition of its neighbours. So the cycle of the trees set the cycle of the chimpanzees. Besides this overwhelming fact, which, we came to realize, was basic to an understanding of the whole of chimpanzee behaviour and social organization, we had learnt a great deal about their dietary habits. As well as the main foods, we had collected a good many samples of species on which they had fed once or twice. For instance, we had found them eating a little red fruit which sticks jauntily out of the ground at the bottom of a juicy green shrub called *Aframomum*; it contains ginger and is eaten by the Africans themselves. And we had found another juicy shrub, with broader leaves than the former, which the chimpanzees (and baboons too, for that matter) broke off at the stem, peeled and chewed: this was *Marantochloa*. One day we had discovered roundish balls made of woody fibres, the size of an apple; even Manueri did not know what they were. Again and again we found them under trees where chimpanzees had been feeding. One day we thought of looking up, and there, all along a branch, we saw a raw strip of inner wood where the bark had been peeled off and its inside fibres chewed up by the chimps, before being spat out. Another plant was chewed and spat out in this way: *Calamus*, the rattan of which chairs can be made, the rattan which we hated, the rattan which barred our way in swampy forest, when the going was tough enough without it, the rattan with needle sharp spikes all along its stem where it nears the ground. It is an odd plant, for although it often creeps along near ground level and does not always climb, only the first few feet near the stem are spiked, and here the spikes are not protrusions from the pithy stem but are part of a jacket which can be peeled off. The chimpanzees, tough as their hands are, avoided the spiky bit and generally broke off a smooth length which they then sat down to chew, or they sometimes just chewed it where it grew. Sometimes they took a bit of rattan with them as they journeyed through the forest, just as the local Africans walk along gnawing at a length of sugar cane, or we Europeans at a stick of rock. I once photographed a chimpanzee crossing the main road, and it was not until we studied it long afterwards that we spotted a food object, probably rattan, in the animal's hand (Plate 6b).

We also tried some food experiments on the unsuspecting chimpanzees, placing fruits which do not occur naturally in the forest on trees and tracks where we knew they might pass, on their way to a fruiting tree. A bunch of ripe bananas was bitten into and individual bananas roughly torn off at the middle of the fruit; none of the bananas was picked off whole, and there was no evidence of peeling. This happened three days in succession. Mangoes left on the ground or put in trees were not touched and were left to rot. Of two avocado pears, one must have had a crack in the skin for the inside was picked clean by ants, the other was moved seventeen yards but we could not be certain what by – it might have been baboons, which almost certainly ate half a dozen maize cobs we left lying around, as we found their footprints and faeces in the area. We also provided the chimpanzees with two unripe paw-paws (big fruits these, looking like a melon); one was totally ignored, and the other was left to ripen, then carried some fifty yards along a chimp track, peeled, and the inside eaten.

Later on, from our notebooks, we estimated that the chimpanzees here in Budongo spend six to eight hours of every twelve-hour equatorial day in the food quest, foraging or feeding. Ninety per cent of the bulk of their diet is fruit, the rest being leaves, bark, pithy stems, and a small proportion of insects – mainly ants which they pick off the bark of the trees. How many pounds of fruit they eat each day we could not, of course, determine, but it must be a good number, for they are big animals (adult males weigh an average of a hundred and ten pounds, females ninety pounds). And the actual number of fruits that pass through their bodies, quite often stone and all, must be staggering, for the forest provides no fruits larger than an apple, and most are much smaller.

Their fruity diet probably supplies chimps with most of the moisture their bodies need, for we only once saw one drinking – up in the trees! It took me a while to work out what he was doing: he was dipping his hand into a hole of some sort and pulling it out and holding it above his head. I looked again and through the binoculars could see drops of water running off his hand into his protruded lips: he had found a natural tree bowl full of rainwater a hundred feet up in the air. Oddly enough it was raining at the time but he didn't stick out his tongue to catch the drops, nor did I ever see a chimpanzee do this, or lick leaves after a shower. The hand-dipping technique was of interest, however, since this method of obtaining water was known to us to occur in the other three apes: the gibbon, the orang, and the gorilla, but had not, so far as we knew, been reported for the chimpanzee.

In their habits of excretion, chimpanzees, in common with all other known primates including untrained man, lacked most of the basic concepts so dear to some other kinds of animals such as cats: the concept of the lavatory, of hygiene, of choosing the moment with discretion, and covering your traces behind you. In short, during the daytime they urinated and defaecated when- ever and wherever they felt like it. And yet there were certain facts pointing to a sense of cleanliness for we found that when chimpanzees defaecated while walking along on the ground, they frequently found a fallen log to squat on. Although we never actually saw this, we were forced to the conclusion by the fact that, of a random sample of faeces which we examined, thirty per cent were by the side of a fallen branch: a higher proportion than could be expected by chance. Was this a primitive toilet habit? It could be, for there is another well-known respect in which chimpanzees avoid contact with their faeces: they do not soil their nests. This has often been reported by earlier observers who found perfectly clean chimp nests, and of the few I was able to examine (most being completely inaccessible) I only once found a little manure on the edge of one of them. We once observed the chimpanzees' early morning practice of defaecating over the edge of the nest: a truly hygienic procedure. Here an interesting com- parison with the gorilla was possible, for the gorilla invariably soils its nest. What was the reason for this difference? Later on we were to go south and see gorillas in their wild, mountain home, and only then was an answer to this intriguing question to come to mind. For the present, we just did not know.

One day we heard chimps calling from a new area where we had never been. There was a good reason for this but we did not know it yet, and when we did find out it was something of a mixed blessing. The hooting we tracked down to a swamp, a horrible, prickly, soggy swamp, covered in mosquitoes, frogs, and evil-looking puddles which, as we soon found out, were infested with a kind of worm which burrowed through the soles of our feet and produced blisters. What we discovered in the swamp was a tree of a kind we had not noticed until now – "Igeria" Manueri called it – with masses of fruits looking like little green plums, and some indeed going slightly pinkish on the outside. These fruits were still unripe, but the chimpanzees had started selectively feeding on them and from their faeces we could see how the ripe ones had been digested and only the stone remained, while the unripe ones had passed through the animals whole. I should explain that soko-mutu, unlike mutu,[1] does not spit out *all* the big stones he finds in his fruit, he eats faster and less fussily than we do, swallowing one here and one there as he goes and spitting out the rest. These fruits were over an inch long and the stones were three-quarters of an inch long.

What we were seeing now heralded the beginning of a new season, the time of the Igerias, and for us (happily we didn't know it) a month in the swamps, the only habitat where this species, the scientific name for which is *Pseudospondias microcarpa*, grows. So, from small beginnings, more and more Igerias began to ripen, the fruits turned reddish and finally a deep dull purple, looking exactly like damsons. And did this mean jam for us? Jam out of those swamps? Hardly; these 'damsons' smelled of turpentine and tasted awful.

This was a time for Wellington boots (incredibly, we had brought ours out from England with us, and we got some locally for Manueri) which, although invaluable in the swamps, were clumsy and caused us to fall a lot on our way through other sorts

---

[1] 'Mutu' is Swahili for 'man'. 'Soko-mutu' (chimpanzee) may possibly mean 'man of the woods'. Or, using another derivation, it may mean 'the man with the ugly face which should not be'.

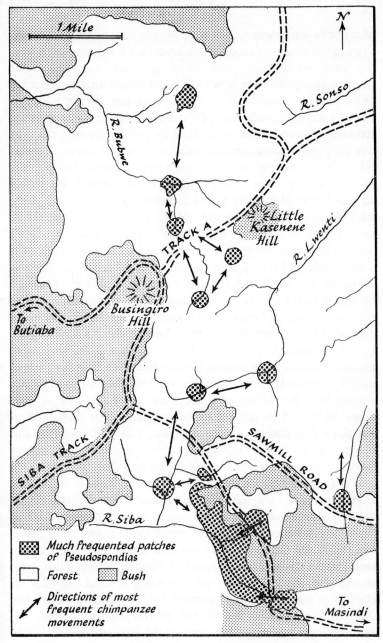

Figure 3. Map showing location of *Pseudospondias* trees and corresponding movements of chimpanzees.

E

of forest to the swamps. This, too, was the time of the ants, which lived in the swamps in teeming millions, criss-crossing high over the water on branches, and dropping down our necks as we brushed along. We were now in the Siba Forest for long stretches (Siba was the name locally given to that part of the Budongo Forest which lies south-west of the main road). The swamps were richer and more Igerias grew there but, unfortunately, the Siba was the place of elephants and buffaloes. More than once Manueri refused to go on and, after an hour's sweating away through the thickets, with chimps calling temptingly close ahead. We would all stand around a heavy round footprint or pile of fresh dung while Manueri examined it and said, with a shake of the head "Hi sasa" – "this is now". He didn't want to believe it and we didn't want to believe it but we all knew it was true and shook our heads a few times and left it at that. For we had been warned about elephants by people who ought to know, and were prepared on this weighty matter to take their advice. Here there was no question of trial and error – our continued existence in this forest depended on our accepting the warnings of those who had gone before. It wasn't so much that either elephants or buffaloes were malicious beasts – no normal healthy beast is malicious to man unless provoked. The danger was entirely that we might walk silently into the middle of a herd, without either our or their knowing it, and be noticed by one animal which would sound the alarm and charge off into the trees, followed instantly, and before we had time to think, by all the rest of the herd, one of whom might run straight into us in the mad dash to escape.

We came to regard some parts of the Siba as hopelessly elephant-ridden; we left the chimpanzees alone there. Other areas farther afield were elephant-free and we now worked in these. We watched chimpanzees arrive daily in twos and threes and fours, and found that they too disliked the swamp-water, for their tracks twisted and turned, following along fallen tree-trunks and any other dry spots, circling around the edge of shallow pools, and crossing streams by tree-bridges where they did not leap across. We plotted their movements from the Budongo and up from other parts of the Siba and saw them pile into a couple of swamp valleys where the fruit was super-abundant; the noise output steadily grew. They fed and fed, with the stones which they spat out and their faeces splashing down into the water below. Some parts of the swamps were drier than others and quite tolerable. We kept to these whenever possible. We saw the pattern of comings and goings we were getting to know so well, and during this period we hit on a new technique, which was to pay big dividends later on. We discovered it by accident: one day we were driving home after work when a chimp crossed the road just ahead. I slammed on the brakes and pulled up, and in the next fifteen minutes twenty-seven chimpanzees crossed the road just ahead of us. We identified each one by its sex and size and any other prominent characteristics, my eyes glued to the road while Frankie, beside me on the front seat, frantically tried to get the information down:

'One big male, pink ears, scar on left leg; one mother with toto (baby) quarter sized; one female in half oestrus . . . pause . . . one old male, grey back; two three-quarters . . .' and so on. The tension would mount as they approached and we heard hooting and drumming close by. Then there would be silence but for my commentary as they burst into view a few yards ahead and walked sedately or scrambled across the road. Manueri was delighted: "Kwanini sisi nakwenda kibirani?" he said – "Why do we go into the forest? We ought to stay on the road!" I chuckled at this thinly disguised plea for easier working conditions, but could not help feeling there was something in what he said. We had got information of a new kind. But it was a fluke: if we stayed on the road all day long we might not see a thing, chimps might not cross that day. It was a quick jump to the question, "When would they be likely to cross?" but as yet we had no answer to that one.

So Manueri didn't get his way just then, but he had planted a seed which would grow. We went on jungle-bashing as before, saw the number of chimpanzees in our area level off and stay steady for weeks, and calculated that we had something like seventy or so chimps in our swampy valleys.

*

Besides our hard-won information on chimpanzee movements around the forest, we had during these first months made many day-to-day observations of the ordinary life of chimpanzees.

This put us in a position, quite early on, to provide a few answers to the most commonly asked questions about this ape, based on our own experience.

Do chimpanzees live on the ground or in trees? It is a question which is often asked. Early reports of their being seen in the trees were often illustrated by woodcuts of a hairy man-like creature standing upright on terra firma with a stick in his hand. In fact, there is no 'either or' about it: chimpanzees live both in the trees and on the ground, are equally adapted to both forms of existence. The amount of time they spend in the trees or on the ground is dependent on such factors as the time of day, and where food is to be found. In the Budongo Forest, the chimpanzees spent roughly fifty to seventy-five per cent of the daylight hours in the trees; at night they slept aloft, and so it could be said that they were somewhat more arboreal than terrestrial. In this respect chimpanzees fall between the more terrestrial gorilla and the almost wholly arboreal orang-utan.

The fact that their food was mostly located in the canopy, and that they spent so much of the day feeding, helps to account for most of the time they spent in the trees. But they also spent long periods up aloft grooming each other, or looking out over the forest or, if they were youngsters, playing tag and other games. Sometimes, when food was fairly concentrated in an area, they moved from tree to tree by an arboreal route, each chimpanzee following the one before at a safe distance, making exactly the same limb movements as they swung between the trees, on branches which looked to us precariously thin. More often, when a move was being made to a new tree, they descended and followed one of their own chimp tracks to a new feeding place. Thus it largely depended on the distance to be covered.

A good test of whether an animal is arboreal or terrestrial is to see how it flees when really scared. If we stumbled on chimpanzees, they sometimes panicked, hurling themselves from branch to branch in great thirty-foot leaps, quickly losing height, crashing to earth at a distance, and galloping off along the ground. This puts them with the forest baboons, as against the monkeys which invariably flee at treetop level. Perhaps chimpanzees *are* more at ease on the ground: how can one tell? But the fact remains that ours spent more time in the trees, and were superbly agile and confident climbers, thinking nothing of walking out along a thin branch and hanging above a hundred-and-fifty foot drop by one hand, while they plucked fruit with the other. Their aim, too, when they swung from branch to branch, flying through the air for ten or twenty feet, was unerring. Not that they *never* missed, however; we twice saw chimpanzees fall. The first time was the most spectacular: having suddenly spotted us, a big male ran out on a branch to leap, the branch broke, and down he came about seventy feet to land with a mighty crash in the undergrowth. Manueri unfortunately chose this very moment to start complaining about the lateness of the hour and how his tummy was rumbling. It was in the early days and we didn't know much Swahili, and we never managed to make a proper search for the fallen chimp; however, he was not near the spot where he fell, and I suspect he was not badly hurt. One thing struck us forcibly: in falling he held his arms and legs outwards and downwards, presenting the maximum air resistance and the best chance for catching on to any branches as he dropped; there was no tumbling in this fall. This falling-posture could be genetically determined, like the falling-posture of cats, although our evidence alone is insufficient to prove it.

The chimpanzees had a phenomenal ability to shin up branchless tree trunks, and a very special means of doing so. Their arms are longer than their legs, as in all the apes, their hands are long by human standards, and we watched how they climbed upwards by using the arms and long hands to grasp somewhat around and behind the tree-trunk, moving each hand up alternately, while the legs provided the upward thrust, the feet being placed on the side of the tree nearest the chimpanzee, small toes one side, big toe the other. This method of climbing is extremely difficult for us humans because our legs are longer than our arms; nevertheless, it is not impossible, and certain Pygmy tribes have mastered the art.

Occasionally we saw a totally different way of moving in the trees, known as 'brachiation'; this is really the gibbon's form of locomotion but chimpanzees can do it as well. With hands clinging to a branch above the head and feet dangling, the body is swung forwards, backwards, and to each side in turn,

	Movement	Ground/Trees	Approximate distance covered
	Quadrupedal Walk Typical quadrupedal limb movements, with weight of body's fore part supported on knuckles; hind feet are placed flat on the ground; relaxed in confident animals.	Both	Any
	Quadrupedal Run Typical quadrupedal movements; at one point all feet are off ground.	Both	Any
	Rapid Run Legs move forward alternately while arms move forward together.	Ground	30 feet plus
	Gallop Fastest run; it is used when the animal hurries to catch up with others or is frightened; limb movements are unclear.	Ground	30 feet plus
	Vertical Climb Arms and long hands keep secure grip on the tree while legs provide upward thrust; feet are placed on the side of the tree the chimpanzee faces; big toe is splayed to increase traction.	Trees	10–100 feet
	Bipedal Walk Rarely used; arms may not be swung in time with the legs but hang loosely down.	Ground	Maximum seen, 9 paces

Figure 4. Forms of locomotion

	Movement	Ground/ Trees	Approximate distance covered
	Bipedal Walk on Legs with use of Arms Independent arm and leg movements; overhead branches allow the chimpanzee to use its arms for added support as it walks on a branch.	Trees	15 feet
	Ground Leap Legs are swung forward under the chimpanzee and land before arms do; e.g. over ditches.	Ground	6 feet
	Vertical Leap Animal uses its limbs merely to check its fall as it drops from branch to branch.	Trees	15 feet
	Swing The arms are extended forward to grasp a branch; the whole body is then swung across; used for moving from tree to tree.	Trees	10 feet
	Brachiation Hanging from a branch, the animal moves along by means of alternate arm movements, swinging the body forward, backward, and to each side.	Trees	20 feet

sed by chimpanzees.

while the arms move forward alternately. This again is almost impossible for untrained humans, whose arms just will not take the strain.

On the ground or on stout branches the chimpanzees usually walked or ran quadrupedally, the weight of the forepart of the body being supported on the knuckles (even high up in trees) while the hind feet were placed flat on the ground. When they ran rapidly on the ground their arms became strangely 'divorced' from their legs, for while the latter moved forward alternately, the arms were swung forward together. Their manner of leaping over ditches at the roadside was extraordinary – flinging themselves forward with arms extended above their heads, they swung their legs forward under the body and landed feet first and fully upright, then swung the forepart of the body down and trotted off. Why they should adopt this complicated procedure is difficult to explain, but I suspect that the fingers and hands are too weak to take the full impact of the body as it lands and so the ape prefers to land feet first.

The most controversial kind of walk of the chimpanzee when on the ground is the bipedal walk, controversial because, being so reminiscent of human walking, it excited early travellers to exaggerate the frequency with which it occurs, producing any number of tales of little black hairy men who walk like people. In fact, bipedal walking is rather uncommon – certainly less common than just standing upright to get a better view. When it does occur, it seems to present no special balancing problems to the chimp, which, at first sight, is surprising. However, watching their movements in the trees, we noticed that they would often walk bipedally along stout branches, supporting themselves from above by holding on to other branches with their hands. Thus the upright body posture is frequently used by chimpanzees. As for the problem of balance, this long, loose limbed creature scarcely seems aware that it exists. Nevertheless, upright walking does make the chimpanzees so fantastically like humans that one cannot help exclaiming. If they walked this way all the time no one but a murderer would ever be able to shoot one. When they do get up it is either because their hands are full or because they want to look over an obstacle or get a better view, but this is not often; they are beasts, not men. Perhaps the nicest comment on bipedal walking was the one we heard in our earliest days, from Xavier, our tracker in the Bugoma Forest. He told us "it normally walks on two legs, but when seen by humans it walks on all four. When you first see them on the ground, they are standing on their hind legs, but they then move off on all four. It *pretends* to move like any other animal."

CHAPTER THREE

The Forest

In the heart of the forest it is quiet most of the time. It is as if every leaf of every surrounding tree was breathing slowly in the moist air, tasting its fragrance. Thin shafts of sunlight fall criss-crossing between the gently rising tree trunks, and scarlet butter-flies move noiselessly from sunny leaf to leaf. One lands on my arm, uncurls its tongue, and tastes the sweat. Some tree-trunks are gigantic, some are small: some round and smooth, others gnarled and coarse; some rotting and ready to drop. It is living so intensely, this forest, that I dare not breathe loudly or give sign of my animal restlessness. Every single tree tells the same tale, of steady, intense growth, no change of view, no desire for improvement, nothing but the calling of the wind high overhead and the answering tap-tap of branches and groaning of boughs. The tree's power is in its absolute steadiness and reliability; I feel vague and shallow by comparison. Yet the tree is stupid and I could cut it down. It has no vain desires, but neither has it any feeling. It accepts death without even knowing it is being killed. Yet I could not cut down the whole forest; the combined strength of all these trees is greater than mine. And I do not want to cut down, or even cut into, a single tree, I just want to feel the huge lethargy with which it grows, the glory of its giant crown, and the final inevitable twisted agony of its death. Every few days I hear a giant crash, and I can tell the distance by whether it is like a cannon or just a dull thud, and whether the ground trembles. That a huge tree, so many tons of timber, which has struggled towards the light, grown broad and spread its branches wide against its neighbours, fruited season after season and fed hundreds of generations of birds and monkeys, drained the soil of its goodness and enriched it with decaying leaves, given shade and fodder to elephants, and provided life for a million insects, that this piece of the structure of the living earth should crash down with unbelievable destruction from its firm unshakable

64

vertical is an event of such enormity and yet such insignificance that I cannot comprehend it, any more than if I witness the death of a fellow human being whom I do not know. Some trees do not fall cleanly, but hang as if reluctant to go, supported by lianas binding them to the forest roof, suspended for a while to rot piecemeal high in the air. Others fall so terribly that they take two or three neighbours with them – young trees of promise but without firm roots. Still others find a purpose in death, forming bridges over streams or gulleys, which will quickly be discovered by the civets and porcupines and chimpanzees.

So, day in day out, as in the population of a giant city, death follows death in a fine random procession. No one notices these deaths except me – I notice a few. And I see too how the saplings and shrubs and lianas and flowers and grasses all rush to close the hole that has been torn in the fabric of the forest roof; species struggles against species, each staking its claim and straining to reach the light pouring in from above. It is a struggle to the death, for only one can finally win, and in the meantime I watch the fungus and beetles and ants begin the task of clearing away the previous occupant which lies now in a position that will never change, growing softer and blacker in an ever-darkening tomb.

*

Other adventurers have been impressed by the forest. One, writing at the beginning of our century, described his reactions as follows:

'For a whole day we crept through the skirts of the Hoima forest, amid an exuberance of vegetation which is scarcely describable. I had travelled through tropical forests in Cuba and India, and had often before admired their enchanting, yet sinister, luxuriance. But the forests of Uganda, for magnificence, for variety of form and colour, for profusion of brilliant life – plant, bird, insect, reptile, beast – for the vast scale and awful fecundity of the natural processes that are beheld at work, eclipsed, and indeed effaced, all previous impressions. One becomes, not without a secret sense of aversion, the spectator of an intense convulsion of life and death. Reproduction and decay are locked struggling in infinite embraces. In this glittering Equatorial slum huge trees jostle one another for room to live; slender growths stretch upwards – as it seems in agony – towards sunlight and life. The soil bursts with irrepressible vegetations. Every victor, trampling on the rotting mould of exterminated antagonists, soars aloft only to encounter another host of aerial rivals, to be burdened with masses of parasitic foliage, smothered in the glorious blossoms of creepers, laced and bound and interwoven with interminable tangles of vines and trailers. Birds are as bright as butterflies; butterflies are as big as birds. The air hums with flying creatures; the earth crawls beneath your foot.'[1]

Thus wrote Winston Spencer Churchill of Budongo, in 1908. Before him, in 1890, the great explorer Stanley had recalled his experiences in the Congo forest to our west:

'I have imagined the forest in listening attitude, the leaves resting in fixed but expressive stillness, and the grey, solemn trees, eloquent of antiquity, a venerable brotherhood involved in silent contemplation. I marvel at the age of the giants, and that impression of durability and resistance which they give.'

And in 1902, Harry Johnston, Governor of Uganda and an excellent naturalist, wrote:

'I love almost more than anything else the forms of vegetation, the effects of sunlight streaming through many different tints of green, the gorgeous flowers on tropical trees, the black masses of mouldering wood, the gleaming white columns of aspiring trees, the emerald cascades of innumerable tiny leaflets, and the huge bold designs in individual leaves and fronds that can be measured in feet and yards; yet somehow or other I feel oppressed and disquieted in these African forests.'[2]

It is not for months that one comes to a deeper understanding of such a forest. Knowledge is the first requisite – wide knowledge of its vegetation types, how they influence each other and together compose the delicately balanced fabrics of the upper and lower canopies and the layers below – the shrubs and herbs. Alas, when we started work, we knew nothing about trees beyond a brief familiarity with the commoner English kinds, none of which occur in Budongo anyway.

[1] *My African Journey*, W. S. Churchill, Neville Spearman and Holland Press (1908, reissued 1962).
[2] *The Uganda Protectorate*, H. Johnston, London, Hutchinson, 1902.

First it was necessary to learn some of the species, but we were ignorant even of what characteristics to look for. Manueri was our source of information. "Miti gani?" we would ask him from time to time, as a particular tree caught our eye – "What kind of tree?" He would look the tree up and down, pick up a fallen leaf, slash at the bark with his panga to expose the inside colour of the bark and of the wood. Some trees exude latex at the slash, others have a distinctive smell, and he would put the bark to his nose. One species has both the appearance and the smell of raspberries and cream. Then he would reply "Hi munyama," and we would note this down, together with a description of the tree's characteristics. Also, if it was a tree on which we had seen chimpanzees feeding, we collected a fallen sample of the leaves and, if possible, the fruit; in this the chimpanzees frequently helped us, for, wasteful feeders as they are, they generally dropped a number of fresh samples for us to pick up. Subsequently these were identified by expert botanists and foresters.

One thing we quickly learnt was that Manueri used the same name for several species of tree. 'Nyakatoma', for instance, was used for two species of fig and one species which had a fruit with a stone in it. If pressed, he would explain that these were "Nyakatoma number one, Nyakatoma number two, and Nyakatoma number three". All the 'nyakatomas' had similar shaped leaves (although far from identical) and all exuded white latex from the slash. The trees he really liked were the mahoganies, of which there were four species. These he would point out to us, with a note of approval in his voice, and would stand and gaze up knowingly at an immensely valuable tree. In all, twelve of the many forest species are really useful timbers, and felled regularly by the mill, while several others are potentially useful. Manueri knew all of these from his days at the mill. He also knew most of the others, but occasionally admitted he was stuck: he would try a few names but they would not satisfy him, the slash told him nothing, nor the smell, and the leaves were ordinary. "Hapana jua," he would say with a grin – "I don't know." On one occasion we had the good luck to be accompanied in the forest by a forest officer, Mike Philip, who told us there probably wasn't a man in existence who could tell every species in the forest at sight. He warned us not to accept Manueri's word blindly, but always take a sample to check on, and gave us valuable tips on species recognition – the shape of the buttresses, the way the branches left the trunk, the position of the tree – whether on a valley, or in a swamp.

As time went by we learnt that many of these solemn trees held secrets. High up on one, an orchid would be seen, nestling quietly in a crotch out of reach of our acquisitive hands. Another would have great outcrops of elephant's-ear fern along its branches – an epiphyte this, living on the tree but (unlike a parasite) not killing it. The larger epiphytes never ceased to amaze us – some species of figs, for instance, are epiphytic, and they grow so large that the result may appear to be a single tree with two different sorts of leaves, one sort belonging to the original tree and the other to the fig. Other figs become true stranglers: they begin life as an innocuous seedling, germinating on a branch high up in a healthy tree; then they send their roots down the trunk to the ground, and the root system multiplies until it entirely surrounds the host tree, covering its trunk almost completely and killing it by sheer physical strangulation. In due course the host dies but cannot fall, being trapped inside the fig. It may rot away at the bottom, so that a hollow structure remains like a little cathedral; higher up bits of the original tree can be seen held in the fig's tenacious grip.

Such sights are the exception, however. Mostly each tree is just a single tree, larger or smaller, fighting its own slow insentient battle with its immediate neighbours for survival. And here begins what is perhaps the most fascinating part of the whole story. Different species have differing degrees of shade tolerance. Thus, while one species thrives in the conditions of prolonged sunlight at the forest edge, shooting ahead of all others, it falls behind another species deep inside the forest where it is forced to grow in almost perpetual shade. And so it is possible, from the species one sees around one, to tell how old the forest is in that particular area.

In 1947, W. J. Eggeling, then Conservator of Forests for Uganda, described in a brilliant scientific paper the natural succession as it occurs in the Budongo Forest, where he lived and worked for many years. Indeed, his first home was on the very spot where we were now based, in a wooden house, for our

stone-walled bungalow had not yet been built. The excellence of
his work was something we only appreciated as time went by and
our understanding of the forest deepened. In brief, he discovered
that the forest was made up of a patchwork of four main forest
types: Woodland forest, *Maesopsis* forest, Mixed forest, and Ironwood forest, plus one minor type: Swamp forest. The youngest
kinds of forest in Budongo are Woodland and *Maesopsis*, both
classed as Colonizing Forest. These are replaced by Mixed forest,
and this in turn is replaced by Ironwood forest, which is the
'climax' type, perpetuating itself thereafter. This process of
replacement is a slow one, taking hundreds of years.

As Eggeling pointed out, the Budongo Forest is growing,
spreading outwards into the surrounding grasslands at a steady
rate of a few yards every year. On comparing earlier maps with the
forest as he found it, he noticed that in many areas grassland had
become Colonizing Forest, and we had exactly the same experience when, fifteen years later, we compared our maps with
Eggeling's.

As a result of this constant expansion, the sequence: Colonizing
Forest – Mixed Forest – Ironwood Forest can be seen, if we choose
the right spot, by walking inwards at right angles to the forest
edge. Firstly, we find ourselves in Colonizing Forest – either
Woodland, which consists of a variety of species, and occurs
where the soil is poor, or, if the soil is richer, *Maesopsis* forest.
These *Maesopsis* trees are easily identifiable by their umbrella-
shaped crowns and their branches which jut out at right angles
to the trunk. This is the tree whose wood smells of cold cooked
chicken, and Manueri's word for it is "Musisi". *Maesopsis* is, in
the jargon of the forester, one of the main colonizing species of
Budongo. As we enter the forest we see first small *Maesopsis*
trees, then larger ones, some real giants – and precious few other
species. This is 'Kibirani toto' – 'child forest', and most of it is
less than a hundred years old. A century ago the area would have
been covered with dense elephant grass.

As we go in deeper, other species crop up with the *Maesopsis*:
giant mahoganies, figs, barkcloth trees, and countless others
which have no English names, and soon there is not a Musisi in
sight anywhere: we are in Mixed forest. What has happened is
that the *Maesopsis* which used to be here have long ago grown to

full maturity and died, being replaced not by their own offspring, which, under their parents' shelter, received too little sunlight to survive, but by the seeds of a whole variety of other species, blown in or dropped in by birds and animals, which were better suited to development in shady conditions. This mixed-up type of forest is commoner than any other type and is the most valuable economically, as well as being the most variegated and interesting one, supporting forty to fifty species of canopy trees and a great variety of wild life. It frequently changes its appearance, and may go on for miles, interspersed by streams and their valleys, patches of Swamp forest, and even the occasional clearing, wholly natural, where for some reason no tree will grow.

But slowly, as we go deeper still into the forest, the first Ironwoods make their appearance, tall and slim, with their deep plank buttresses on which the chimps drum (Plate 11b). First one, then a small group of them, until finally almost every big tree in sight is an Ironwood (*Cynometra alexandri*). We are now in the oldest type of forest, the 'Kibirani Kubwa' or 'big forest', on ground which has supported nothing but trees for centuries. There is little herb and shrub life, it is as though these trees extracted every scrap of goodness from the soil. Clear a patch of these trees and Woodland or *Maesopsis* will grow: the whole sequence must start again. There is little animal life on the Ironwood Forest floor because, apart from the annual fruits of the Ironwoods and a few isolated shrubs, nothing edible grows there. And yet, paradoxically, the fine tracery of Ironwood leaflets allows a good deal of light to filter through to the forest floor – more than in Mixed Forest. Why then does so little grow beneath these domineering trees? The reason is still imperfectly understood, but it is probable that other species are unable to withstand the competition of the Ironwood's shallow, but extensive and highly efficient roots; shade, at any rate, does not account for the failure of other trees and shrubs to regenerate here.

It is fascinating to look at a map of the forest types and speculate on the causes of their present-day distribution. Why is the whole forest not pure Ironwood by now? Why do patches of *Maesopsis* occur deep inside it? In certain cases we know the answer, where areas have been cleared relatively recently in connexion with timber extraction; in others we do not. Doubtless, small-scale

5. Even on branches over 100 feet high, chimpanzees rest their fore-parts on their 'knuckles'.

6a. Chimpanzee swinging from one tree to another.

6b. A male crosses the main road with a food object clutched in his hand.

clearing of the forest to make villages may have occurred in former times, but there is no actual evidence of this in the form of village ruins among the trees.

Soil samples taken inside the forest have, however, been found to contain traces of charcoal and pottery fragments, and it may be that some seven hundred years ago much of Budongo was grassland inhabited by Bahima cattle grazers who, around that time, were migrating slowly southwards along the sides of the rift valley. Clear evidence of their passing has not been found in Budongo, but in the Bugoma Forest to the south there exist the remains of one of their kraals, now covered in trees. At that time, during the thirteenth century, Budongo may have been no more than a number of patches of forest standing where Ironwood Forest stands today; in the meantime these patches have grown outwards and joined together. This would mean that most of the forest is fairly young, for at present only some thirty-two per cent is Ironwood Forest.

Additional evidence that much of the forest is young is provided by the termites. The tall mounds of grassland termites, often as high as a man, surround Budongo and are a very constant feature of open conditions throughout Bunyoro. These termites (*Macrotermes bellicosus*) cannot survive in forest. Eggeling described, and we too found, many disused, overgrown grassland-type termite mounds in the youngest forest types – Woodland and *Maesopsis*. As *Maesopsis* gives way to Mixed Forest, the mounds become less prominent, being flattened, rather like tiny hillocks, as a result of the combined influence of rain- and leaf-fall. In Ironwood Forest there is no sign of the mounds of this species. If we knew the time it takes for a termite mound to change its shape from a tall, slim tower to a scarcely perceptible bump, we should have a rough chronometer for the forest.

But we do not know, and there are no records of any kind to help us. Even tree-rings, when they do occur, cannot be correlated with years in this land of perpetual summer. So the questions of the age of the forest and the extent of human habitation remain open for further study. Only the most recent history is at all certain. The African sawmill employees say that until they arrived as immigrant labourers early this century the forest was shunned by man, and this is undoubtedly true. Certainly there

F

are no pygmies in Budongo, although they live in the Congo nearby. Did they ever live in our forest? It is impossible to know: there are not even any traditions, for the populations of Bunyoro have moved about, of their own free will and under pressure from the British government, which in 1912 declared the area north and north-west of Budongo an uninhabitable zone on account of sleeping sickness, and moved the entire population elsewhere. Thus while the patchwork quilt of forest types mirrors the forces which have been working on the forest for centuries, there is no certain way of telling which of these pressures were natural and which man-made.

*

The Budongo Forest is rain forest, it is tropical rain forest, and it is semi-evergreen tropical rain forest. What is the meaning of 'semi-evergreen'? In England we use the word 'evergreen' of conifers, of species which do not shed all their leaves in winter; those which we do not call 'deciduous'. In Budongo, there are neither conifers nor winter, nor any situation resembling the one we are used to in the temperate zone. The leaves of all species are not shed at one time throughout the forest; each species has its own habits, and the forest as a whole always looks green. This makes it 'semi-evergreen' in contrast with true evergreen forest, such as the fir forests of Scandinavia, in which the individual trees never shed all their leaves at once, and true deciduous forest in which, as in English woodland, winter sees every tree stripped of its greenery.

In Budongo the process of shedding is amazingly rapid. In many species, such as the 'Mukunyu' fig, there is less than one week between the time the leaves drop from their twigs and the time their tender replacements sprout forth; sometimes the old leaves seem to be pushed out by the new ones. The time of year when this occurs is very variable. Other species have more familiar habits – 'muvule' (*Chlorophora excelsa*), for example, is truly deciduous, having a wholly leafless period from time to time. The most extraordinary species, however, are those in which some whole branches shed all their leaves at one time, while other branches may be all budding, and others still leafy. Such trees look raggedy brown-yellow-green all the year round and are an affront to the beautiful symmetry of their neighbours.

In its own complex way the forest is very much alive. The briefness of a human life-span is such that we can scarcely observe more than the growth of a single tree, but studies such as those of Eggeling have shown us that the life cycle of each tree is part of the cycle of the trees of other species, and the cycle of all species combined is the life cycle of the forest. In our lifetime the Budongo Forest will grow. Time was when it did not exist at all: time will be when not a tree remains.

*

Tropical rainstorms have often been described, but what is less well known is how a forest affects rain. It does not simply cause rain-bearing clouds moving over from beyond the forest to condense, but it actually seems to cause the initial formation of the clouds in a windless blue sky, filling the air with moisture until it is saturated and can hold no more, at which point the sky empties itself, pouring back on to the forest in minutes all the water it has absorbed during the preceding hours.

The afternoon rains are the most spectacular, and we watched the cycle with fascination from our hill. After a clear blue sky all morning, during which all the crispness of the air is sapped slowly away, and the clear calls of birds fade to a deadness in the droning sticky air, noon finds the forest shimmering with a layer of hot haze above the dark green transpiring canopy. The sun is now directly overhead, and temperatures are approaching their high-point for the day. The heat is intensely oppressive at this time: sweat will not evaporate, and the morning clothes which are hanging out to dry retain their wetness despite the blazing sun. Lizards bask on the rocks in our garden, flowers stare out boldly on the trees, their scent trapped around them in the steady air. Only down in the cool forest below are animals on the move. Outside this is a time of rest.

At about two o'clock white flecks appear out of nowhere in the sky, and at the same time, very gently, the air begins to move. Tiny puffs of white, high in the sky, ride along unnoticed unless you search for them. By three they are bigger and turning grey in the middle, suddenly one blots out the sun and every living thing takes note. They are moving overhead quite quickly now, from the north-east, and the pattern of their shadows moves over the treetops which stand quiet and still. Slowly the sky loses its battle and clouds blot out the last fragments of blue, turning now from white to an unpleasant grey. Down below the moving mass it is suddenly a trifle cooler but none the less humid; a first roll of thunder is heard, and the rest follows swiftly. The wind, as if it could no longer be contained in the upper air, falls to ground level and curls the treetops. Menacing black clouds ride by just overhead with enormous speed, suffused by an evil yellow glow. And then a curtain, with ends blurred at either side but clear as a knife-edge along its lower rim, appears in the distance over the forest, moving closer at a leisurely pace, blotting out little hills here and there, then silhouetting a ridge as it reaches the valley beyond, before that ridge disappears and the next in front of it is silhouetted in turn. The curtain is light-grey, and as it nears our hill a faint hissing can be heard above the sound of the wind; this is followed by the rat-a-tat of the first few drops on our corrugated-iron roof. The cats go indoors, doors bang, thunder peals and crashes overhead. Lightning shows like brief gold streaks against the black forest sky. Our skin turns to goose-pimples in the cold and as the curtain passes overhead, the stampede of rain on the roof forces us to shout to make ourselves heard. We are shut in now, a little unit of people against an African force. Wind lashes the rain and I see the forest outriders, great trees and thinner ones, swaying jerkily and out of time. Unabated the drumming overhead goes on, as if the water were trying to batter the place down. The whole air smells deliciously of rain; I sit with a mug of tea on our verandah, perfectly dry, smelling this gigantic torrent three yards in front of me. It is the same feeling as the Triumphal March in *Äida* has on the people in the front row. And like the great music of *Äida*, it has to end, and the end is not a final brilliant overwhelming smash, but a dying off, a sighing regret. The sun quickly comes out, and as anywhere else after the rain, the colours are brighter, the air is fresher and the birds begin to sing.

But the forest is cold after the storm, and each of its millions of leaves is coated with a film of water. As the sun breaks through and the air above the trees grows slowly warm, white vapour forms in the treetops and drifts idly upwards to the clouds. The forest looks as if a thousand campfires were smouldering below the trees. This is the rising mist which comes after the rain, and which has led to reports of 'steaming forests' in travellers' tales. It is true that the forest steams, but the steam rises from tree-top level, not from the ground. Inside the forest the air is clear and cold after rain, and a million raindrops fall from the leaves above. Looking up, one sees the treetops enveloped in swirling mist. It is only from outside the forest that the vertical shafts of mist can be seen, rising towards the clouds. This rising mist is quite separate from the mist of early morning, which lies in long banks along the valleys and over the sea of leaves, looking at times like a mantle of snow. This is a true ground mist, here elevated by the trees to a hundred and fifty feet up, which occurs on cloudy mornings and is gone by the time the sun has climbed half its way to the top dead centre of the sky.

Rain fell on seventy per cent of our days at Budongo; on about half of these occasions it was really heavy. Sometimes we were able to watch it from the verandah at Busingiro as I have described, but most often, naturally, we were down inside the forest itself. "Mvua!" – "Rain!" was Manueri's simple and meaningful remark when he detected the first signs. "Mvua?" we would invariably reply, looking up at the cloudy sky. "'Pana sikia?" – "Can't you hear?" We strained our ears and heard, faintly above the bustle of the leaves, the distant hiss of that rain curtain. These storms were always a messy business. We had plastic macs but they were torn from the start and after nine months made little difference. At first Manueri had no protection but we bought him a mac, for although he huddled under a tree-trunk, small and motionless, during the storms, as he had done for years, it was unfair to expect him to head for anywhere except home after it had stopped, especially because of the demoralising effects of the 'second rain' – the dripping of leaves and showers from saplings that we knocked as we walked along after the storm was over. This second rain soon soaked his shirt and shorts and made him shake his head sorrowfully about his rotten luck. He looked askance at the green plastic coat the first time we gave it to him, then grinned and put it on. It even had a hood. Out of habit he squatted down as the rain hit us, and tore a huge gash in it. Then he discovered, as we had done, that if you squat down in a plastic mac, or adopt any position other than the vertical, water collects in the folds and spills into the inside through the gaps at the front between the buttons. Further, as we also knew, it is almost impossible to stop water getting in at the neckline. Still worse, one tends to heat up and get itchy if the coat is well and truly sealed up against the elements. And then if, in order to protect the ears, one covers them in plastic, there is a constant humming and crackling sound and one cannot hear anything else.

Looking back, I doubt whether Manueri was any more impressed with this latest triumph of civilized man than we were. As time wore on and little was left of his coat except the pockets and a few tatters of plastic held together by the seams, 'putting it on' became more of a ritual than anything. Perhaps he wanted to show us that he had not lost it, or perhaps he wanted a new one. But we could not afford new ones for him or ourselves and as they fell to bits we simply got wetter and wetter. Towards the end we did not take them at all but sat during the rain just like chimpanzees, knees bent, arms folded over knees and head resting on arms. In this way only our backs got wet through.

The worst thing to do, as we discovered one day, was to keep moving. We had been heading for the road where we had left the Land-Rover when the storm broke. It was a toss up: whether to shelter or press on. We none of us knew quite how far it was to the road, all we knew was the direction. It was tempting to think the road was near, just beyond the farthest trees we could see. We pretended to recognize trees. In five minutes we were wet through. It was a heavy storm, great trees were creaking between the thunderbolts, threatening to hurl down branches and crush us in an instant. Manueri had seen this happen and he truly feared falling trees. We pressed on, our wet clothes filling up with water, our binoculars filling up with water and the camera getting wet, our shoes slipping in the mud and our glasses misting over. We tripped on unseen lianas and fell into the mud; it was too late now to do anything but go on. The rain was cold on our bodies and we shivered convulsively. Images of the dry comfort of home tantalized us. Where was the road? Unbelievably, we cut through a patch of undergrowth and there it was, the red gash of the road, the channels on each side aflood with swirling water. Our legs felt heavy and the trousers clung; getting into the car we sat on sodden bottoms feeling miserable. Five yards were enough to tell me something was wrong with the car. I got out wearily, back into the teeming rain. We had a puncture in the rear tyre. The rain didn't matter any more somehow. Manueri got out to join me, and laughed as we jacked up the car: "Mimi mekanika, nataka shillingi" – "I am a mechanic, I want more pay." He helped mainly by just being there, a fellow sufferer, and the rain was not half so bad, or the frustration when the wheel nuts proved to be rusted on tight. Frankie sat in the car and shivered. When we got home Semei, our camp guard and general factotum, laughed and asked if we had been swimming in the Sonso. We looked at him in his clean white shirt and khaki shorts, perfectly dry with his hair brushed, and felt strangely proud of the tough, comfortless way we lived out there, under the trees.

CHAPTER FOUR

Creatures of the Forest

In the Budongo Forest we slowly uncovered a secretive animal life of astonishing diversity. It might have been possible, by extensive reading, to have prepared ourselves for each discovery, so that we would have had nothing more to do than confirm our expectations, with a pompous "that's a such-and-such" and a self-congratulatory pat on the back each time a new species came our way. Instead, we entered the forest largely unprepared, except for the bigger game.

For instance, we knew from Game Warden John Blower that there were many elephants and buffaloes in the Budongo, that leopards were common, and that there were plenty of deadly snakes, such as the Gaboon viper and the python. We also knew of the extremely shy forest duikers, the monkeys, and the wide variety of birds. And of course there were the chimpanzees.

But the forest had entirely its own way of disclosing what it chose to let us know. For the first month or so it told us nothing. We cut into it and hauled our unfit London limbs through it and occasionally watched the chimpanzees: this was, in the narrowest sense, our work and we concentrated all our efforts on to it. At that time we had everything to learn, or perhaps not to learn but to re-learn. For it was faculties we had had in our childhood and since lost which now were of the utmost importance. We needed to use our eyes and our ears and our noses, we needed to walk silently over the twig-strewn forest floor, we needed the poise of flexed muscles and agile limbs. And, above all, we needed to learn the pace of movement which is most suited to travelling through the forest, a pace which varies from one forest type to another, according to the number of obstacles and the usefulness of animal tracks. We learnt from Manueri how to recognize these tracks – how to tell the elephant's – wide and high – from the buffalo's – narrow and high – and from the chimpanzee's – narrow and low, and antelope or pig tracks – intermittent. Along each track we learnt to read the two signs, dung and prints, which each animal must leave wherever it goes. Elephant droppings and buffalo-pats, chimpanzee droppings and those of the duikers and bushbuck and pig – each has its distinctive appearance, and gives a clue to the time since the animal was last on the spot. This latter is an essential factor in deciding whether to press on when elephants or buffalo are about. The foot-prints add further information, telling us which way the animal went: here again, this information is of vital interest in the case of elephants and buffaloes.

From Manueri we absorbed the basic techniques of travelling and tracking in the forest, but he always knew and observed more than us, right up to the end. "Hi nini?" we would say to him, a hundred times a day – "What is that?", and he always knew, even if he found it exasperating trying to tell us. For instance, I remember a day in August, when we had been wandering for six months in the forest and were beginning to feel confident, that we kept finding little heaps of roundish balls of what appeared to be chewed-up fruit-remains on the forest floor. "Hi nini?" I asked Manueri, to which he replied with a gleam in his eye, as if he was sure I wouldn't understand, "Hi ndege" – "It is a bird." I could hardly follow his description of the bird, but it seemed to be quite a big one. Why then hadn't I ever seen one? I asked. Because, he proudly announced, they fly at night only. Now I thought I was on the track, it was some kind of owl, and I was finding the pellets. At home I checked my bird books but found no fruit-eating owl. For more than a week we found the fruit-spittings every day. I gave up thinking about them. Then one day Manueri volunteered, "Hi ndege sasa nyama" – "it is a bird like an animal." Of course! They were bats, fruit bats; Manueri was delighted that I knew. "Ah, mimi najua, mimi najua," I kept saying, over and over again – "I know, I know" – and then I began a quite lengthy attempt to explain how bats were not 'birds like animals', but were true mammals, having no eggs but live young, while Manueri tolerantly listened to my painful Swahili, nodding his head seriously at the idea and secretly rejecting it. Manueri was like that: too old to change his views. He knew so much that was perfectly right and correct, the few mistakes he made were of no importance. His language, in this instance, distinguished "ndege" – the birds, things which fly, from "nyama" – animals, things which walk; it did not leave room for bats.

The forest is full of signs, if you can read them. We learned the smell of civet cat, under trees where civets are sleeping, and the look of the civet's 'lavatory' for like true cats (from which it differs in many ways, for example in being a fruit eater), it uses a particular place or places to defaecate. We learned the smell where chimpanzees had been feeding. From English zoos we knew the smell of elephant droppings – it was just the same. We learned to spot overturned leaves, which indicate that an animal has been past since the last fall of rain. We learned to distinguish the alarm bark of the bushbuck from that of the baboon – the latter often having a slight intake of breath after the bark. We learned to distinguish the twittering of the Redtail monkey from that of the Blue, and the totally different deep gargling roll of the black and white colobus. By ear we came to distinguish and know about a hundred kinds of bird calls, but we could rarely identify them.

And slowly, diffidently, a little here and a little there, the forest began to disclose its secrets. For months we did not see any flower on the ground. Then walking into a glade, we found a beautiful russet bottlebrush plant standing all alone. Flowers are rare on the forest floor. Apart from the bottlebrush, there were pale blue flowers like pansies hiding under leafy banks, tall slender mottled-green lilies, and lovely violet convolvulus bells which trailed among the bushes. Butterflies, which emerged only during the heat of the day for a few hours either side of noon, provided another source of colour in the green-brown trees. The most striking is the kind which is crimson-winged; if you sit in a sunny spot one will generally come and settle nearby in the warmth. The older ones are raggedy and orange, like painted old women in Les Halles, in Paris, but those in their prime have a pure redness which is the more striking for its green background. Higher up, bigger butterflies move in the treetops, some a foot in wingspan, but these are rare. The real place to see butterflies is not in the forest itself but on the tracks through it. Here it is sunny and they course up and down all day, settling every now and then to look for food. And their preferred diet, the delicacy which renders them drunken, stupid with ecstasy? Dung, excrement, urine, all. We saw hundreds of them, twenty species at a time, clustered on small pieces of dung, side by side, jostling for position, and not letting outsiders in to join them. Swallow-tails, yellow or green with black dots, indigo-winged beauties which changed to a dull leaf-brown as they closed their wings – all bustled and gorged themselves together, the dainty guests at this, to us, sordid banquet. With our fingers we could gently pick them up; with a throw of the net we could catch them all; with one merciless blow from the tyre of our Land-Rover, we could wipe out every one.

Fabre, in his famous book about scarab beetles, has adequately described how we humans feel at this juxtaposition of the beautiful and the beastly. Modern science has, of course, no time for such romanticising: it sees the biological world in terms of life cycles, the utilization of food sources and perpetuation of species. And, scientist or no, it is only the first time that one notices that swallowtails feed on dung that one feels the incongruity. We accepted the fact quickly, the more so because dung, to us, became a source of information and so lost its repulsiveness.

Dung-beetles were numerous in the forest. Attracted with incredible rapidity to any fresh manure, they arrived from all directions, crashing to earth by the food and burrowing into it. None of the ones we saw ever rolled dung-balls, however, as the sacred scarabs studied by Fabre did. Ours were either black or, more often, a shiny metallic green colour, and were mostly small except for one black giant who was two inches long. Within minutes fresh dung was alive with them, and within an hour or two it was gone. They fed inside the forest, in its cool depths, and not on the open tracks where the butterflies held sway. Giant moths were another feature of our forest, although we only once saw one. We were sitting on the verandah of our home one evening when what I thought was a bat flew in and landed on the mesh door. Looking again, I could hardly believe my eyes. Something was staring back at me – it was a moth with eyes as big as my own, sham eyes, vivid painted rings in the middle of its brown wings. An Emperor moth. It was dazed and allowed me to measure it quite calmly: eight and a half inches from wingtip to wingtip! Too precious for us to risk its sudden death on the

Tilley. We turned off the light and shook its perch and off it flew, back into the forest night.

Flies were abundant throughout the forest, some like our own house flies, but with brilliant red eyes. The largest, popularly known as 'elephant flies' were true giants (Africa has a giant of everything), black, white, and green in colour and an inch long. But of all the flies we met, the horseflies made the deepest impression on us, mentally and physically. April and May are their months, and I remember being warned of them by a visiting forest officer earlier in the year. But somehow one never heeds a warning, and where there are snakes and elephants and leopards, who could care about a fly? Suddenly they emerged, fully grown, and congregated on the foliage on each side of the forest tracks. At first there were tens, then hundreds, and then thousands of them. And the most amazing thing was that it was *movement* that attracted them. Thus, walking up a forest track, we would be besieged by a great swarm of them, but when we stopped and stood perfectly still they went away. And herein lay the great and awful paradox: whether to move and get home bitten, or stay still and get nothing and nowhere at all. Most of the time we ran, collecting flies in thousands; they clung to our clothes and faces and hair. And being adapted for sucking the blood of buffaloes and antelopes, they had no difficulty in penetrating our bush-jackets to the skin underneath. Each bite hurt with a piercing momentary pain; automatically we swiped and killed the flies which were slow to escape, but the swelling and itching could not be avoided. They favoured our ankles and wrists and we wore bracelets of red bites which took a week to subside. Fortunately neither of us reacted strongly to them; some people have to be hospitalized after a number of bites. I can see them in my mind's eye – long, thin flies, with wings neatly folded over their backs, like English horseflies only slimmer – and I hate them.

But there was an even deadlier enemy waiting for us in the forest. An enemy which marches in a column of unimaginable length, and which, moving inexorably forwards, may take a day and a night to pass a given spot; an enemy with organized military equipment in the form of soldiers with huge jaws which clip shut and never reopen, even in death; an enemy which consumes every living thing in its path that does not escape before it is dragged down; every portion is eaten except the bones. I mean, of course, the safari ant. Suddenly, plodding through the forest, Manueri (always up in front, poor fellow, and he knows it) shouts "Dudu!" – and we run, on, forwards, through them. We had, of course, to develop this technique; the first time we just stopped in the middle of them and gazed at the seething forest floor, while our legs slowly started going black as the ants crawled up us. That was the first time: the first time is always the most memorable and in this case it was the most painful.

Having run out of the swarm, we strip off our bush trousers and throw them aside, then pick furiously at those which have got inside and clipped themselves securely into our legs. The smaller workers come off easily but the big soldiers do not – we pull off their bodies and their heads remain firmly clipped on. It is fifteen minutes before we are on the move again.

And then there are the ticks. Fortunately, owing to our clothes, we are not unduly worried by these, but every now and then one manages to slip through. And ticks, bless them, have an uncanny knowledge of human anatomy, and always manage to find their way to a peculiarly intimate part of one's body, there, with one final heave, to embed their heads into the skin, clip on with pincer jaws which cause no pain, and proceed to suck themselves blue in the abdomen with one's blood. In the evening one finds them, while having an all-over wash. The question arises: how to get rid of them? All one can see is the blue-red abdominal blob and four pairs of legs on each side (for the tick, like the spider, has eight legs), so that the whole thing looks like an ugly flower with half its petals missing. It will not be pulled out. In our little booklet on tropical health we searched, the first time, for information. I had the tick and I felt affronted by the presence of this creature attached to me which I did not want. The book said that if we pulled the hind-end off, the head might fester; the tick had to be persuaded to budge, all of its own accord. Two ways were suggested: by dousing it with paraffin, or by applying a burning cigarette end to its bottom. It did not mind the former, and I could not stand the latter. Result: on this and every other occasion we pulled the body off, leaving the head in. None ever festered, and one gave me a pleasurable itch to scratch for months afterwards.

The most surprising insect constructions we found were beautifully made chimneys, which occurred in clusters of a dozen or so around the base of trees, deep in the forest. Six inches high, they were perfect tubes of soil, brought up from below the leafy humus, made with extraordinary precision from a series of mud rings piled one on top of the other, perfectly round, about an inch in diameter at the base and tapering very slightly. We had no idea what creature it was that had made these; the chimneys we examined were always empty and there was nothing below them. Later we learned that these mud-tubes were probably made by emerging cicada nymphs. These nymphs lie underground, feeding on the sap of roots; in some circumstances, where surface conditions are unfavourable for their final metamorphosis, they construct these earthen chimneys and remain in them until ready for transformation into the adult insect: the buzzing, whirring, whizzing cicada we knew so well.

There were many other buzzing creatures, such as dragonflies and beetles of all sorts, cicadas and lantern flies and wasps, too many to describe them all. One extraordinary insect was the 'buttress fly' as we called it – a creature with a tiny body, long spindly legs and fine wings, which lived only between the plank buttresses of giant trees – at least, that is the only place we ever came across them. When we first noticed them they were always moving up and down, slowly, drifting about in the dim space between the buttresses, but as we drew nearer and they detected our movements the speed of their movement increased: the distance they went up and down grew less, and they moved much more rapidly, as if quivering with excitement.

There was a kind of insect which had an even better technique for warning us off: believe it or not, it tried to intimidate us with *sound*. It generally happened like this: we would sit down, for lunch or to listen for chimps, and would become aware of a rhythmic rustling in the leaves close by, a sound which was just like the footfalls of some stalking animal, slow and regular. After a search we could find the cause – a large number of termite soldiers were beating with their heads among the leaves and beating in unison. If seriously disturbed they lost their rhythm but quickly picked it up again; if we kept still their whirr-whirr grew weaker until eventually the symphony stopped.

Termites, occasionally, swarm. This we discovered in no un-certain way when, waking up in the middle of the night, we discovered nasty squashy insects crawling all over us. A flash from the torch gave us some idea of what was happening; when the lamp was lit there was revealed a seething mass of little bodies crawling in at every crevice around our closed mesh windows and under the doors – millions of termites creeping in on us to share our warmth and our bed. There was nothing to do but retreat. We tried the next room, laying a paraffin barrier behind us, but it was no use. So we moved to the last room, barricaded the crevices and cracks with paraffin-soaked paper, systematically executed every 'dudu' in the room and finally dropped off into a light sleep, broken every half hour or so as one of these wretched insects wandered over our faces. It was a horrible night. In the morning we surveyed the carnage inside the house; outside the windows and doors was a canopy of silver wings, million upon million of them; we picked them up in handfuls and let them slip like silver snowflakes between our fingers, glinting in the morning sun. And their bodies being good to eat (Africans consider them a delicacy; we tried them fried with onions and they tasted like tiny shrimps), all the walls and corners of the house were covered with ants, spiders, wasps, and other carnivores of the insect world carrying the termites off to their food-stores for future con-sumption.

There was one beetle which was so magnificent that I must tell of him. He dropped to the ground beside us one day, in the Siba forest, scuttled under a leaf, and lay still. He had hit the ground with such a whack we were both startled, and when I uncovered him we saw what a beauty he was: brown and white and green and black, *Goliathus goliathus*, the goliath beetle, largest in the world. I picked him up, put him in our polythene lunch bag, popped it in a breast pocket, did up the button and forgot about him, leaving further examination until we got home. I did not for a moment think that my victim would be uncomfortable in his new surroundings.

It was an hour or so later that I suddenly felt something on my neck. I put back my hand and felt this enormous hard insect. With wild infantile imaginings I let out a shriek and tore off my jacket, cricking my neck badly in the process. For once I was scared out

of my wits, and the whole episode is stamped irrevocably in my
mind. The beetle came off with my tangled jacket: he was not in
the least harmed, just looked at me as if surprised at his own
power, making me feel ashamed. He had cut through the polythene and crept out of my pocket, scared me, and won my
respect: I never once thought of harming him. I wanted to take
him home for a photograph, but I also felt the need to know
where he was at all times. I finally decided that both he and I
would be quite safe if I kept him in my handkerchief, dangling
from my hand.

Back at home, I put him on a log, with a matchbox to show his
size, and took a snapshot of him (Plate 8b). It was easy, for he was
slow and unable to walk well, his feet being specially adapted with
twin claws for climbing vertical tree-trunks. Just after the camera
had clicked, he sprang with a whirr like a toy aeroplane up into
the air, sailed once majestically around the house and then,
straight as a die, headed off towards the Siba, one mile away,
towards the exact position where I had picked him up. How he
did it I do not know, but that beetle must have possessed a
wonderful sense of navigation, as bees do.

Talking of bees, Budongo has them too. One day as we were
walking home through the forest Manueri suddenly stopped and
said "Asali" – "Honey". His head was cocked on one side; we
listened, and could faintly discern the hum of insects; following
him we traced it to a fallen tree. There were three separate holes
in the rotten trunk, and at each bees could be seen entering and
leaving. It was a scoop – Manueri's face beamed with delight.
Next Saturday he would return with fire. Poor bees!

We accompanied him to see how it was done. He had picked
a bunch of grasses outside the forest and had, as always, a box
of matches. In addition we carried an empty 10-gallon oil drum
for the honey: he assured us there would be lots of it. Fortunately
the tree was not far inside the forest or we would never have
found it, but there it still was, with the bees humming to and fro.
Where did they find the flowers, I wondered, thinking of the
dank brown and green forest floor we knew so well, where
flowers are rare or not at all. And I remembered the canopy
where millions of tiny blossoms, visible only from above, appear
on one tree or another all the year round. That in turn tallied

7. Dawn over Budongo.

8*a*. A small frog.

8*b*. A large beetle.

8*c*. Python digesting a duiker.

with the fact that bees were very rarely met with on the forest floor; here they had come down to their nest, but as each bee left it flew upwards to the canopy again. Some bees probably never come down to ground level, for we had come across nests way up in the trunks of living trees – these, with a shrug, Manueri had always left behind and forgotten. Here, at last, was a nest on the forest floor: manna from heaven.

So under each hole he placed grass, and gathered sticks to catch from the grass, and lit the grass which flared up merrily. We stood well back, having discovered that these little forest bees did not have a correspondingly mild sting; they had resented our presence near the nest: what would they now be like as their home caught fire around them? But it did not catch fire: the rotten wood simply smoked as the flames licked around it. Manueri stood by the tree cutting into it with his panga. Every now and then he pulled a bee off his neck or arms, but the stings did not seem to bother him much. Feeding the flames and cutting, he worked inwards towards the nest. Bees were now pouring out in their thousands and Manueri worked on among them unperturbed. Within minutes he had hold of the first honeycomb and shouted that it was "mzuri" – full of honey, and it went into the drum. Others followed in unimaginable quantities – if they were all full of honey I guessed we would have gallons of the stuff. The bees collected around the drum with its honey-smell and began to go into it; more and more bees kept coming in. Manueri now started a fire under the drum, for he said that unless the bees were killed they would eat all the honey. After an hour's work at the tree the last honeycomb had been removed and the drum was nearly full. It was hot now and the remaining live bees were suspicious, flying around and around but not going into the heat. Covering the drum with a jacket, we left the thing to cool down and went off home. I took the lead with the panga: Manueri's hands and arms were puffy and paralysed from the stings.

In the afternoon we returned with vessels for the honey and muslin to strain it through. Bees were still around in small numbers, which increased when we removed the jacket and the honey smell escaped. We had to work fast. The scene inside the drum was hideous: about three feet solid of dead bees on top,

G

then the wax of the honeycombs, congealed and formless, blackened from the soot of the fire, all of which was thrown away, and underneath the sooty golden honey, dotted about with bees and small lumps of wax. This we poured straight through the muslin into the bowls and pots we had brought: there was less than we had expected, about a gallon in fact.

The carnage of the friendly bees had been appalling but we were hungry for the honey; we saw that we had worked in cold blood and were not ashamed. Great was Manueri's delight and the delight of his friends and our delight when we ate the honey, that day and the next and for a couple of weeks thereafter.

*

The bird-life of the forest is heard rather than seen. My immediate memory is of a constant backcloth of song, harsh cries and softer tones weaving their way to us through the trees in a complex multi-dimensional pattern, for birds are not static, and so, as one listens, their voices move close or out of range, drowning others, or allowing them, like hidden notes in a symphony, to dominate despite their timid tones. And all one sees is the trees, the leaves falling. One searches and searches for a bird, any bird, but sees nothing. And then, suddenly, a red or violet streak moves against the green and is lost again instantly.

It is not possible to make any generalizations about the birds in the forest. There are big birds and small ones, brilliantly coloured birds and dull brown ones, noisy birds whose voice carries half a mile and quiet ones whose faint babbling scarcely reaches the ground. Among the biggest is the giant black-and-white-casqued hornbill, an extraordinary bird whose casque (the protuberance of horny substance on top of the bill) is a giant resonating chamber for its extremely unpleasant, harsh voice. A Uganda folk-tale relates how the hornbill came by its voice. Once upon a time the hornbill had quite a nice voice, but she was so vain about it, and was always trying to sing such high top notes, that her voice broke, and unfortunately all her children inherited it, and now they are forever telling the other birds and animals what a beautiful voice their mother once had, and how much it was admired, and all the jungle is tired of hearing about it.

At first sight the hornbill is an amusing creature, looking like an overgrown magpie. Because of the size of its head and bill it always looks top-heavy, and, seen from below, it has the shape of a cross, head and tail extending an equal length from the wings, which move up and down at perfect right angles to the line of the body. Generally it caw-caw-caws as it goes, and its wings make a rushing sound, not musical like a swan's or whistling like a duck's, but just plain flap-flap-flap as if the bird was making heavy weather of it. And with such an un-aerodynamic shape goes the splendid Latin name for this bird, *Bycanistes subcylindricus*, which somehow manages to convey the Heath-Robinson quality of the whole job. I was prepared to see one break down at any moment, yet the things obviously didn't mind flying because they were to be seen winging their noisome way across the forest in ones, twos, and threes at all times of the day. Whether the bird is ugly or not is a question each person decides for himself; my own view is that the closer you get the uglier it becomes, but seen at a distance against a backcloth of forest it makes an attractive picture. Two types of black and white hornbill were present in the Budongo, one, the Uganda type, with a square-fronted casque and black central tail-feathers, the black reaching the tip of the tail, and the other the Congo type or white-thighed hornbill, with a pointed front to its casque and a white band across the end of the tail. The existence of these two distinct yet broadly-speaking very similar types, raises again the fascinating problem of the history of the Budongo Forest, how long it has existed, whether it is a remnant of a much wider forest, and at what points, if at all, it was once joined to its vast brother, the Congo rainforest which now lies to the west, beyond the Albert Rift. The answers to these questions are speculative and there is no agreement among scientists. If we could know more about the subject we might be able to plot the movements of animal species and show how different forms have emerged through isolation from one another. As it is, the existence of the two hornbill forms, sharing a single niche in this forest, tells us little more than the fact that long ago the ancestral black and white hornbills became split by an unknown geographical barrier, perhaps the great Rift Valley; that they remained apart and developed certain differences of casque shape and tail pattern, and that now, whether by migration of the hornbills or by movement of the forests themselves, the two types occur together in this locality.

Enough said about the hornbill, and yet it was the only bird which seemed to believe in self-advertisement rather than self-concealment. A big bird but much less often seen was the black-billed turaco, at once a brilliantly coloured bird and one which cannot be seen until it flies. The body and outsides of the wings are light olive green, and while feeding the bird moves about in the branches by rapid sinuous runs and jumps, keeping perfectly hidden. The effect of its colour and speed is that the eye is unable to follow the bird and one simply does not see it. Perhaps if there were not always some movement of the leaves one would. But then, suddenly, it flies, and the unfolded wings shout their violent scarlet message: it was the most powerful colour impression the forest had to offer.

At the other extreme was a bigger bird, the crested guinea fowl, which, despite its bright blue and red head, is beautifully camouflaged in a dark greeny-blue mantle of feathers, speckled with little blue-white spots. An elegant example of adaptive coloration this, for no colour-combination could be better for a bird which spends most of its time moving around the forest floor, among the deep shadows, the dark greens and blues and browns. Unlike its grey-coloured, open-country cousin, the tufted guinea fowl, this forest bird keeps very quiet most of the time. Its call is so soft that it can only be heard when the fowl are very close to, and it lacks entirely the harsh, carrying, rasping call which the bush fowl makes as it settles to roost in the evening. During the first months of the year the fowl were in flocks in Budongo, and we would bump into twenty or thirty birds together; later, in April, the flocks became scarcer and pairs were the rule, and then in May and June the pairs would be accompanied by their broods – anything up to ten little chicks trailing after their parents. As the young grew older they quickly came to look very like the adults but they had not yet learned caution, and sat about on branches they had flown up to, gazing at me as I stood below, gun in hand. But they were as yet no use for the pot – all bone and feather, very little flesh.

A noisier game bird was the local race of francolin, whose rasping call we often heard, especially at roosting time. This little African partridge is brown with white spots all over, and has a brilliant red beak and red legs; but it is much less numerous than the guinea fowl. And lastly, I once only saw yet another species of red-legged fowl or partridge in the forest, which came pecking past me as I sat watching some chimpanzees. There were two only of them, and from the description I made of them I later identified them as Nahan's forest francolin, a shy and uncommon bird.

There were other brilliantly coloured birds, some with metallic hues, such as the broad-billed and blue-throated rollers and purple-headed glossy starlings; others were dull like a violet bird[1] I watched one evening, as he sat deep in a valley on his white-soiled perch, flitting up to take a fly and landing again, flitting up again and landing, as the forest grew misty and cold.

But one's memories are mostly of sounds. There is the soft song of the blue-spotted wood dove which, starting on a high note, and repeating it a few times, lets it fall with increasing tempo and then, when it touches bottom, brings it up again, slowing the tempo as it does so, until it hits the first note again, which it repeats slowly a few times just as it did at the beginning of the phrase. To think that such a cadence, which might have inspired a romantic composer such as Dvorak or Ravel, is merely innate behaviour, an unthinking response! There was only one bird whose song was better, the white-browed robin-chat, which lived outside the forest and whose liquid tones came in phrases, which began ever so quietly as if the bird was a long way off, and then built up to a great crescendo of unbelievable intensity, which suddenly stopped. It was as if the bird were singing as it flew towards you, and yet I have watched the whole performance, which occurs at dawn and dusk, and seen the bird sitting perfectly still at the bottom of a bush, only its throat heaving as the music grows louder and louder. I do not want to deny the beauty of our nightingale's voice when I write about these African birds – for I believe the nightingale is a finer singer than either of them;

[1] *Melaenornis edolioides*, the so-called 'black flycatcher'.

the beauty of his song is in its unpredictability, whereas these other two repeat a sequence over and over again, and thus one inevitably tires of them in the end.

There was the yellow-bill, a close relative of the cuckoos, that laughed a shrill cackling laugh which mocked us as we cut our painful way through the swamps, with rattan spikes tearing at our fingers and arms and pricking us teasingly through our clothes. There were four kinds of cuckoos; birds that boomed a single penetrating note; woodpeckers that tap-tapped at the trees above us; and a strange repeated note from a bird we never saw, sounding like a whip flying through the air and coming down with a crack. Manueri said this noise was produced by a squirrel so perhaps it was not a bird after all. And there were the parrots. These were mostly grey parrots though some were a green colour, and we rarely saw them by day. They were most impressive in the evening as they flew in parties, high overhead, to roost. I do not know where they roosted – perhaps, like the hornbills, they left the forest at night to sleep in the surrounding open ground. But every evening they would fly over quite high, their pure calls, interspersed with wheezy squawks, drifting down to us in the forest below. Short, quick wingbeats they had as they sped by, and the falling of their notes out of the violet, gold-rimmed sky had all the magic that is Africa. After them, the dragonflies appeared for their dusktime feed, a few moths and bats emerged, and as the creatures of the day curled up and crawled into their sleeping places, those of the night were stirring and smelling the air and peeping out of half-open lids at the encroaching night.

*

Then there is that strange cold-blooded half-world, as it always seems to me, of snakes and frogs and slugs and slimy things. One such was a kind of 'snail–slug', neither one nor the other but a bit of each, which we frequently found on the broad-leaved shrubs of the forest floor. This creature was brown, an inch or so long, and looked like a slug with a hardened, flat spiral-shaped disc on its back. It really did seem to be an intermediate stage between the slug and the snail – either a snail in the course of losing its shell, perhaps exchanging this form of protection for an unpleasant taste, as the slug has done, or to be a kind of slug in the course of evolving a true shell into which it would one day retreat; but this creature lacked the ability and even the tendency to contract its body under the shield when touched.

Tree frogs were common, mostly small, and they came in a wide variety of colours: one which I photographed was an inch long, handsomely turned out in leaf-green livery with spotless white knee-caps. Often as we walked along small ground frogs leaped out of the way of our descending feet, missing death by inches. We rarely had a good view of one of these but once we did succeed in catching one and bringing it home. I cunningly arranged for it to leap, on its release, into the neck of an empty chianti bottle, then stood the bottle right way up and was satisfied to see that the creature could not escape. It was about the size of a sixpenny bit, and khaki coloured. I wondered what it ate, and decided that the little ants, which were crawling in columns up the walls of our house, might be suitable for it, so I caught a dozen or so and released them in the bottle. Then I pushed in some grass and twigs and a bit of earth, and hoped Froggie would be happy. But he wasn't. He hung glumly upside down near the top of the bottle below the neck, disregarded ants which crawled under his nose, and leaped blindly against the bottle walls whenever he was disturbed. We could not keep him; his natural dignity was gone; we derived no pleasure from the spectacle of this now thoroughly dirty frog tumbling in the bottle. So we let him go.

Exactly the same happened with the tortoise. There were two little blue-shirted, khaki-trousered boys, the eldest of the huge family of Marco Okenyi, the local Game Guard who had at the very beginning introduced us to chimpanzees; he had moved house since and now lived just down the road.

These two boys went to school every day, and on their way they had taken to coming up to our house with a bucket, and in the bucket there was always something different, either tomatoes, or bananas, or maize, or avocados; but the price was always the same: fifty cents (sixpence). We generally bought the goods, and the boys walked away. They were always solemn, one only spoke. He looked at me as his father looked at elephants, and he took the little silver coin. They asked no questions and neither did we, but treated each other in a businesslike way.

One day there was a tortoise in the bucket. The boys did not seem surprised and the price was the same. "Natoka wapi?" I asked – "Where does it come from?" "Kibirani tu," the talking boy said, jerking his head slightly towards the forest. It was no use asking him to take it back; he would probably just let it die in the bucket. The boy's two deep eyes were burning into me without a doubt that I would take the prize. We looked around. There were boxes, the ones our food arrived in every week from Masindi. I picked up the tortoise, which was a land tortoise, clean and in fine shape, but he would not put out his head to look at me. He must have been newly caught. We gave him straw and paid off the boys; normal life resumed. But for Gogo, as we called him (after the Swahili for tortoise: 'nyamagogoto'), life had taken a turn for the worse, and he was not a depressive tortoise who would sit with his head in and suffer: he fought back. Time after time he got his front legs on the side of the box, heaved himself up to the edge, then fell with a crash on to his back, where he lay until one of us put him the right way up again. We gave him water to drink but he stepped on the edge of the bowl every time and made a mess. And what, we wondered, does a land tortoise eat? After trying everything we had in the house and everything that grew in the garden, we finally found that a mixed diet of tomatoes and bananas set him eating busily. We built him a brick-walled enclosure in a corner of our verandah, so that he could walk about. And we used to let him out when we were on the verandah, watching, so that he could walk about and puzzle the cats.

But Gogo remained unhappy: it was obvious. He still tried to scale the brick walls. One day he succeeded in pushing off a top brick and clambering through the gap. We found him at the edge of the garden, defeated by a vertical slope: he had been heading straight towards the edge of the forest. After that he escaped again and again. He had huge resources of strength on the luxury diet we were feeding him; he could heave bricks around like a builder's mate. Gogo did not like our verandah and he did not want our hospitality. In addition, we had used him for an experiment with the chimpanzees, putting him in their path to see their reaction (there was none, incidentally: they just walked straight past him), and so we could not justify keeping him any longer. One day Manueri and I took him down to the edge of the forest and let him go. He wanted to snuffle about in the leafy depths and find his own suppers, he was sick of tomatoes and bananas; he made this clear to us, and we gave him his liberty.

A worse fate befell Sally. Sally was an olive house snake, eighteen inches long, with a silken skin and beady yellow-green eyes. She was friendly to humans, but death to geckos and lizards, which she caught, constricted, and ate whole without a flicker of emotion, two or three times a week. Sally was a gift to us from Janet Stoneman, a snake handler in Masindi, who obtained snakes from local Africans and caught some of the deadliest ones herself, such as mambas, for an agent in Nairobi who supplied zoos all over the world. There was no great demand for Sally at that time, however, and she had been in Janet's care for long enough to be fully accustomed to crawling around on human beings and exploring them intimately – all one had to do was relax and not make any jerky movements which she might misinterpret. While on the move, Sally lived in a little gauze bag, and at home we put her in a big box with plenty of straw and a gauze top attached around the edges with drawing pins. It was this method of attachment, though I did not know it, which was to prove our loss and her undoing.

For weeks she worked with us. Her role was a simple one, and she did it splendidly. She had to lie on chimpanzee tracks, preferably wriggling a little, so that we could observe the chimpanzees' reactions to her, in order to see whether they would instinctively fight shy of a live snake, or investigate one, or even attack. In order to achieve this we were forced to tether Sally to stop her slipping away, but we did so by a completely painless method: a piece of sticky plaster was wrapped around her tail, and to this a fine cotton thread was attached, on the end of which was a stone too big for her to move. (Gogo had been tethered in a similar way, but to a much larger stone, since he was immensely strong.) As long as Sally was in the shade she did not mind this. And we made the perhaps significant discovery that no chimpanzee ever came near the snake, although we were unable to prove that any ever avoided her, since we never saw them anywhere near her! It is entirely possible, however, that their eyesight had detected her at a distance and that they had then taken another route.

Sally lived with us and consumed our geckos for a month or more, and during this month our two cats and four kittens took to sleeping during the heat of the day on the gauze roof of Sally's box, in a cool back-corner of our verandah. Unknown to us, the weight of the cats was slowly forcing the gauze downwards, and where it was pinned at the edges it was tearing. One morning Sally was gone. We quickly found the cause, but we did not find Sally. We looked under every stone, we cut away the long grass. We felt she was nearby, as on previous occasions when she had escaped she had never gone far, usually hiding under a big fallen leaf or in a tuft of grass. But this time she had beaten us and we gave her up for lost. On the sixth morning after her escape a sorry sight greeted us on the verandah: Sally was distributed about the place in bits and pieces an inch or two long. She had been nearby all the time, but that night the cats had found her and had instinctively killed. Poor Sally! She may even have been on her way back to the box to see if there was a gecko inside it when she died. I looked at the kittens dozing innocently on the gauze, the carnage of Sally strewn about them, and could not be angry.

Sally was a nice snake; every other snake was not. We often saw them crossing the road – bright green boomslangs, four feet long and with big, staring eyes, or small brown night adders, speedy and venomous. There was the green one that climbed up Manueri's leg, a large black cobra which we disturbed one day as it basked in a patch of sunlight deep in the forest. I myself shot three snakes with the ·22. The smallest was a black-lipped cobra, sleek and black, a very slim five feet in length, with white bands under the head and neck. I came across it one evening while out looking for guinea fowl. It lay like a stick in my path, then raised its head as I approached, giving itself away. I shot it in the neck and it died immediately, although it writhed involuntarily for some time. The second in size was a Gaboon viper, deadliest of Africa's snakes, which, while normally placid and therefore harmless, can, if it bites, kill a man in less than an hour. My shot did not kill it instantly, for it disappeared into tall grass and I had to leave searching for it until next morning. When we found it it was only two feet away, dead, but still writhing a little. The snake was heavy and, even in death, still dangerous, for a touch of its fangs could still kill. It was three feet six inches in length and ten times as fat as the cobra. Its gape was wide – to swallow the large forest rats on which it fed. The pattern on its back was extraordinarily beautiful – blues, yellows, reds, and blacks were balanced against each other in a symmetry without parallel in the animal world or even perhaps in art; the brightness of the colours meant that it had just changed its skin. As we picked it out of the grass on that sunny African morning, the horror I felt at its fangs and gape, combined with the ugliness of its arrow-shaped squashed-flat head with little pig-eyes well concealed, together with the unquestionable extreme beauty of its skin along the length of the back, inspired in me a sense of awe for the thing, which my African helpers shared.

If I were to be asked why I killed these snakes, I would have no trouble in answering and my answer would be completely truthful: I killed them because I did not want to run the risk of meeting them again. It was as simple as that: dead snakes do no harm. But in the case of my third snake, the python, everything, from start to finish, was completely different. For a start, I did not bump into the snake, I was led to it.

The story had started the night before. We were at home having supper when a labourer from the Forest Department came to the house. "Nyoka kubwa sana," he said it was, "a very big snake", and I guessed it was a python. Would I come next day to kill it? They would be grateful to me if I would kill it for they were working in the area and were scared of it. I said I would come and look at it, but how could they be sure to find it again? They said it would stay put.

That night I thought about the python, down in the forest, not knowing how dangerous his position was. In a way, although I wanted to see him, I hoped he would move off so that we would not find him. I had no desire to shoot a python, for they are inoffensive towards man. I awoke determined that, if we found him, I would film him and leave him alone. Two men arrived and, accompanied by Manueri, we set off. The snake was deep in a part of the forest I did not know. It took an hour to reach

the spot – ahead I heard the tracker cry "iko!" – "it is here!"
Coming to the spot I saw my python, his head raised angrily at
the intruders, his sharply pointed, big tongue flicking in and out,
tasting the smell of us, his terrible foe, perhaps the only animal
he was afraid of. He was totally immobilized by a huge animal
he had swallowed, and which now lay in his stomach distending
him beyond belief. His head and a couple of feet of neck were
free to move, the rest of his body behind the stomach lay coiled
underneath him. He stared at us unceasingly. We stared back. I
spoke to Manueri and the African trackers, "Hi nyoka muzuri,
hapana kali. Hi hapana weza kukamata mutu" – "This is a good
snake, not dangerous. It cannot kill man." They shook their
heads "Hi kali sana" they said. "It is very dangerous." "Mimi
nataka piksha tu," I said – "I only want to take a photograph
of it."

It was early yet. There was time to wait. The two men would
get fed up with waiting and go off, then Manueri and I could go
home. I told them I should be waiting there until the sun was
high in the sky, then I could take a better photograph. They
settled down to wait with us. It was a strange situation, us four
men, me with a gun, they with knives, and this immense snake,
more powerful muscle for muscle than any of us, but paralysed
by its huge digestive capacity. We leaned against tree-trunks or
on our elbows, waiting. The men puffed at cigarettes, and talked
in Lunyoro. I watched the snake, which did nothing. Inside it
was some sort of antelope. I could see the shape of the animal's
head, which had gone down first, and the twin points of its horns
which were almost breaking through the python's skin, then came
the bulk of its body: swallowing that huge mass must have been
as painful as having a baby.

I watched the forest coming to life, as it does every morning,
its tempo and the hum of its insects increasing imperceptibly as
the temperature rises. As always in the forest, the odd leaf fell,
birds sang near and far away, giant motionless tree-trunks stood
all around. Only this time there was the snake. And (I should
have realized) patience is the African's virtue, it is the one thing
he has in abundance, and it is a quality all white men lack, to a
greater or lesser extent. I set myself a deadline for departure at
noon, and in its own good time noon arrived and the snake was

still there digesting, and the Africans were still there sitting and talking, and I was still there. So I got up, took my photographs, called to Manueri and announced our departure. At this they were indignant and shocked. It would surely kill somebody; they wanted it dead. If necessary, one of them said, he would kill it with his panga. I looked to Manueri for support; he averted his eyes. That told me I was defeated. They would do it. I imagined the scene: it would be too terrible for words. I considered taking it alive, but we had nothing to put it in and it would be a colossal burden with that beast inside it. Added to which I had no experience in handling live pythons. Regretfully, after a lot of talk, I decided the most humane thing would be to kill it. If I left it I would have its death on my mind anyway: better to do the job properly. I moved towards it with the gun raised. Alarmed, it suddenly struck out with its mouth open, displaying rows of white teeth, all its free neck lunging forward. Again and again it struck, so I had to aim from a distance, and even that was not easy, for I wanted a side shot and the snake kept its beady eyes on me. I felt it was imploring for mercy, pleading me to go away. Finally it looked away. I squeezed the trigger, dispatching with that tiny bullet one of the most splendid creatures I have ever seen.

We carried it home strapped to a pole. It was eleven feet six inches long, eleven inches around the neck, thirty-three around the stomach. Then we skinned it; it had a pair of sharp claws, one on each side of the anus, or genital opening, which, according to Manueri, were used not only in mating but also to grasp hold of the victim's nose, whereupon the snake would fill its nostrils with excrement and suffocate it. As we slit open the stomach there was revealed a fully grown female red duiker, almost undigested. The smell was awful, and the snake was using a variety of worms to help it in the process of digestion. We left quickly; a few days later I returned to collect the teeth of the python which had by then been picked clean by insects. I also took the duiker's skull; I am looking at that skull now as I write; its bone is blackened all over by the acid juices of the snake.

*

Few people know what mammals to expect when they walk into the forest. We ourselves had very little idea what we might see. For the forest fauna is very different from that of the surrounding plains: zebras and hartebeestes and gazelles and sables and giraffes and rhinos and many of the other animals one thinks of as typically African, are absent. Lions and, oddly enough, hippopotami do occasionally occur in Budongo, but this is exceptional. The reason is not hard to find: Budongo lies at the top of an escarpment below which are Lake Albert and the three-mile-wide flatlands around the edge of the lake. These flatlands are typical open bush country containing herds of antelopes and lions; hippos live in the lake itself. The odd lion or hippo which finds its way up to the forest has, for some reason, abandoned its home ground and headed eastwards. Elephants abound down on the flats and, being expert climbers, often come up the escarpment and into Budongo; in 1924 it was estimated that the forest supported a herd five thousand strong. But they do not stay in the forest all the time – there is a continual coming and going of elephants northwards of Budongo, probably as far as the Murchison Park where they are fully protected and hence extremely numerous.

Most of the forest species, however, live in the forest and do not leave it. This is almost certainly true of the forest buffalo, which come out of the forest to rest in the tall elephant grass at its edges but browse inside the forest, where they make trails in the same way as elephants do. There are two kinds of buffalo in Africa, the red Congo buffalo of the forest and the large black buffalo of the plains. In Budongo the latter kind is found, showing that it is able to adapt to forest conditions. Buffalo did, however, seem to be most common in the Siba, where the forest is largely riverine and allows them easy access to the surrounding grassland. As elephants do with their tusks, buffalo damage trees by debarking them with their horns, and eat the tender rind of saplings, for I have found such trees stripped bare minutes after buffalo had left them. Fortunately, we only once had a close brush with one of these great beasts. We had been making our way in silence towards some chimpanzees in particularly dense woodland forest when suddenly there was a thudding of feet and something rushed past us rather too close for comfort. We saw nothing.

"Hi nini?" I asked Manueri – "What is it?"

"Sijui – labda nyati" – "I don't know, perhaps buffalo."

All seemed quiet again so we went on. In due course we came up to the chimps and I remember we had just settled down to watch a mother and her youngster when the crashing started up again, and, again completely invisible, something big tore past us not more than ten yards away.

"Hi nyati moja – hi kali" – "That is one buffalo – it is dangerous," said Manueri. Without more ado he chipped a series of steps in a low tree by making one neat vertical and another horizontal cut, hauled himself up and invited us to follow, which we did. All this was just too much for our mother chimp, who rapidly built a nest for herself and her baby and clambered into it. And for fifteen minutes or so there we all stayed, three scared humans in a small tree and one scared chimp up above; if the buffalo was watching from a nearby bush he might have been pardoned for a bovine expression of smug self-satisfaction. At all events, we heard no more of him.

Another animal which finds its whole living inside the forest is 'chui', the leopard. Little is known about the habits of this secretive cat, and although I believe leopards are probably fairly common in Budongo, we were rarely favoured by a glimpse of one. Once we had been watching a group of chimpanzees for some minutes, high in the top of a tree nearby, when suddenly a loud rustling of leaves came from behind us, we looked round and saw first a duiker in headlong flight and then a leopard, some ten yards behind, chasing it in great bounds through the undergrowth. Neither of them saw us, and they were gone in a flash, yet this brief scene imprinted itself on our minds.

Manueri, returning one day on his own along a forest track, came face to face with a big leopard in the act of eating a blue duiker. I wish I could describe the scene as he did. "The leopard looked at me, I looked at him. He growled. I had no panga, not even a small knife with me. But he wasn't hungry, he just wanted peace. I turned and walked away a few steps, I waited. The leopard got up, the duiker in its mouth, and walked off the track into the forest. Inside he growled. I heard him eating. I edged past the spot *poli-poli*, very slowly, and then I ran!" He enacted every stage in the drama with gestures and expressions;

we could imagine the scene very well. At the end came a moral: It is not good to walk in the forest with no knife, and he admonished himself for his stupidity.

Armed with his panga, however, Manueri was unafraid of leopards, as we discovered on two separate occasions. The first time he came home one day with *half* a red duiker, the front half to be exact. I asked where the rest of it was and he said he had come upon a leopard having his dinner, shooed the leopard off and grabbed the dinner. The second time we were deep in the forest, all three of us, when suddenly there was a dreadful scream quite close by. Without any hesitation, Manueri started off at high speed towards the scream, leaving us to follow. When he reached the spot where he thought it had come from, he stopped and looked all around and up in the trees, but we found no sign of anything, no blood, no signs of a scuffle anywhere. Manueri was certain we had heard a leopard making its kill and he wanted the meat; perhaps we had. What we had definitely discovered was that Manueri was quite prepared to walk up to a leopard and dispute matters with it; whether this was bravado, folly, or an intimate understanding of jungle lore we were less sure.

Three species of antelope occur in Budongo, all fairly common. These are the bushbuck, the red duiker, and the blue duiker. Bushbuck spread beyond the forest into the surrounding savannah, but the duikers do not. All three are hunted with snares on a very large scale, although this is illegal and the game guards do their best to prevent it by dismantling any snares they find. The ram bushbuck is, when fully adult, an extremely beautiful creature, standing some thirty-three inches high at the shoulders and with fine, gently curving horns rising upwards and outwards in the shape of a lyre. Known as the 'swara', it provides a man with two months' food and is thus highly prized. We saw bushbuck quite often, sometimes very close to. Once, out looking for guinea fowl, I turned a corner on a forest track and suddenly came face to face with a bushbuck, a fine adult male, not ten yards away. For a second or two we surveyed each other, and then he sprang into the trees, barking loudly in a deep, harsh, penetrating voice as he crashed through the shrubs. As he leaped I saw the fine white stripes along his sandy-coloured flanks, stripes which have the unusual feature that they do not occur in a fixed pattern, for some animals have few while others have many, and some have horizontal stripes as well as vertical ones, or even spots instead of stripes, breaking up the coat and thus providing camouflage.

The red forest duiker or 'churo' is especially common in Budongo. Its coat colour is a deep rich russet all over, the male has straight, ringed horns about six inches in length, reaching fine points, and stands about eighteen inches high at the shoulder. Like all the duikers, the 'churo' walks with its back curiously arched, giving it a hunched-up appearance. The alarm bark, which is all one normally knows of this elusive creature's presence, is a single repeated harsh note, higher pitched than that of the bushbuck; it is an ugly sound, strange, coming as it does from one of the forest's loveliest creatures, perhaps *the* loveliest. We rarely saw one for long, just fleeting glimpses as it crossed the track ahead of us or scampered through the trees. Once, however, as we were sitting silently waiting for chimpanzees to call, a pair came picking their way daintily between the shrubs, stopping to snuffle in the leaves; they did not sniff us and went quietly on their way. Tragic that this lovely thing should be the tenderest, sweetest meat the forest has to offer: it was a sad tale which taught us this.

We were returning home from a day in the forest. I was out with a strange tracker that day, Manueri being ill with blisters on his feet. Suddenly we saw a red duiker by the side of the track, and as we looked we saw him trying to free his head with a hind leg. He was snared. As we approached he struggled violently, his eyes showing white, with a piteous fear of the men who were now closing in to murder him. I looked at him, and decided not to release him as his neck was sore from the rubbing wire and would fester, and he was bleeding around the face from trying to free himself. The tracker got a forked pole and pinned him down, then throwing him on his back I cut his throat with the panga, the only weapon we had. It was a horrible business and confirmed my belief that snaring is cruel; I was glad of the dozens of snares I had dismantled, some of them rusty with lack of visiting.

Having done the deed we handed the duiker over to the men, who were delighted. We kept a leg for ourselves, and discovered

H

it was like veal, light in colour and fine-textured. I regret to say
the horror of its end was quickly forgotten; nevertheless, I never
hunted the red duiker despite its table qualities, for I had no
desire to kill one as it picked its harmless way through the trees.

Equally fascinating was the blue forest duiker, one of the
smallest of the ungulates. Thirteen inches high at the shoulder
in the adult, with a pair of horns an inch long in the full-grown
male, this little blue-grey coated creature wanders about the
forest flicking its tail wherever it goes. There are thousands of
them in the Budongo Forest, and they move around singly or in
pairs, although on one occasion we saw four together and on
another, six. 'Nende', as it is called, the blue duiker is a charming
toy antelope, specially adapted to browsing on the very lowest
level of vegetation, the delicate young leaves near the ground,
leaving the higher ones to the red duiker and those higher still
to the bushbuck. Once, in a rainstorm, a blue duiker sought
shelter under the very tree where I was standing, and for a
moment I felt that thrill of purity which St Francis must have
known, and which is shared to greater or lesser extent by everyone who has contact with wild animals: it was as if the duiker had
no fear of me. Of course, the instant it sniffed me and caught my
eye it was gone, flashing into the rain like an arrow, and my
illusion was shattered; I was sad. Manueri in particular used to
enjoy staying perfectly still as a 'nende' came by. He would
whistle softly to attract our attention and we would see his lips
pointing; following we would spot the animal walking along, as
all browsers and grazers do, a few steps and then a bite, a few
more steps and another. Inevitably, at close range the duiker
would smell us and, with hooves clattering over the sticks and
leaves like the noise of a toy train, squeaking in a high-pitched,
shocked voice, it would dash off into the trees.

As with the red duiker, it is a cruel paradox that such a lovely
thing should be the chief target of humans with their snares, of
leopards, and of the python. Between them, the duikers keep the
forest's predators supplied with food, they are little more than
walking dinners for the carnivores. Other species benefit from
this: the monkeys and chimpanzees, the rats and shrews, and all
the other forest creatures which might fall prey to the carnivores
if it were not for the duikers. So their place in the jig-saw of

forest life is very clear-cut: they are born to be crushed, bitten to death, and snared. Fortunately, they do not know this: fortunately, perhaps, we none of us know the fate which awaits us. It seems an irony of nature that she created them so beautiful, but beauty is in the eye of the beholder, and the irony is in the mind of the person who sees the beauty. To the local African, as to the leopard and python, a duiker is meat, the meat he craves, and he will go to great lengths to secure it.

One day a tall man was on our steps when we came home. In his arms he held a young 'churo'. The sun was beating out of the sky and sweat was pouring off him. He said it would be tender and tasty; we were angry with him and thought of the mother. The baby duiker struggled feebly in his arms. We bought it and for the next week fought a losing battle to keep it alive. It was still on milk but we had no teat and no way of getting one, our imitations, using gloves and other things, did not work. But worse still, it clearly did not like the milk we were giving it, which was, on the advice of a local European who had successfully reared a duiker, half milk, made in our usual way with powder and water, and half water, with a dash of salt. The poor little thing hated this, much preferring my armpits which must have smelled right but were, alas, utterly unable to provide him with milk. We knew we needed real milk. Near by were some villagers who kept a herd of goats; they said that one of their goats had kids and that next day they would sell us a bottle of milk. But next day they said that it was impossible, the kids needed the milk and had taken it all. Our baby was weakening. The nearest herd of cows was fifteen miles away. We raced to the farm and waited until milking time at five o'clock. Arriving home we force-fed the duiker but we had little hope for its recovery. Later in the evening it had convulsive spasms and I could see it was suffering badly so I shot it. If we had taken it back to the forest when we first bought it, a mother might have heard its bleating and adopted it, but it might have fallen victim to a leopard or starved to death. Our mistake had been to feed it on dried full-cream milk which was not suitable for it; we had lined its stomach with fat, preventing further digestive processes. Naturally we had tried feeding it with solids but it had never eaten a thing, not even the tenderest young shoots we hopefully collected from the forest for it every day. It was just too young; and we told the man angrily he must not do it again – we did not want another baby, of any species. He must have been sorry, for next day he presented us with a tin-bowl of flowers.

A creature which died rather more suddenly was the giant edible rat which Manueri trapped on his own doorstep. I think he was trying to catch a bush pig, which used to come in the night and snuffle around on our refuse pile. He never succeeded. We did, however, get a wart hog. A neighbour and I had been out looking for buffalo in the Siba – he was a big-game hunter and had a heavy rifle. On our way home we spotted two wart-hogs in the tall grass just outside the forest. He fired and got one. We heaved it into the Land-Rover and, back at home, Manueri displayed his skill at butchery: the panga was all he needed. As with the duiker, we ordered a leg, and roasted it; the texture was as of pork but the taste was a little strong, and reminded me of the smell of the animal when it was in the Land-Rover, freshly killed. We did not finish the joint.

But to return to the bush pig, or, to give it its more attractive name, the red river hog. Quite unlike the wart hog, this is a beautiful animal. We only once got a good view of one. It was a full-grown specimen, two and a half feet high. Suddenly, without a sound, it stepped out on to a forest track just ahead of us. It didn't see us as we stood, not twenty yards away in broad day-light, but came out confidently, showing off its bright orange-brown coat, and walked into the forest on the other side. In those few seconds my whole attitude to pigs was changed: I had now seen the stately majesty of a fine boar; our domestic pigs with their rolls of fat are hideously degenerate. The natural beauty of this hog, the ease and directness of his silent walk, was a far remove from the slobbering grunting swine of English styes. Once again, Manueri had no such fanciful ideas. He threw up his arms in despair as it calmly disappeared. "Wapi bunduki? Wapi bunduki?" he cried – "Where is the gun?" He had seen, in that pig, meat for himself and his friends for weeks. There was the difference. I was living off meat which I could afford to buy, although, of course, he could have afforded it too if he did less drinking. Manueri was in favour of my carrying a gun at all times and he frequently told me so. I told him it was an encumbrance and this was perfectly true. But my real reason was that I did not want to let fly at every thing that moved; I was a conservationist and my stomach was well lined. Manueri's attitude was much less complicated.

Then there are the monkeys – four species in Budongo, and all of them common, so that you are almost certain to see them on any day spent in the forest. The little redtail monkey ('Kunga') is the most charming, with its snow-white nose in the middle of a black face, trim moustache, white cheeks, and long rusty-coloured tail. Always affronted by your presence, they sit chirping like birds and making rapid movements of the head, running a little way, intensely curious and not a little scared. If you pass on they do not scamper away, but they dislike being looked at and quickly head off into the trees behind if you stop. We only once clearly saw one of these on the ground, it walked with its long tail held vertically and curled over forwards at the tip. Much is known about the redtail monkey, thanks largely to the efforts of Alec Haddow, who made a special study of its behaviour, during which he discovered that it played a part in the transmission of yellow fever by mosquitoes to man.

A close relative of the redtail is the larger blue monkey, locally known as 'kima'. A shy creature, its coat colour is grey-blue all over, with a black crown, and just below this, in front, a very distinctive white stripe above the eyes. Very little is known about this species. A fruit-eater, like the redtail, here in Budongo it spends much of its life in the trees. Once again, there was only one occasion when we saw a blue monkey on the ground: it was deep in the forest, and as he fled up into a tree just ahead of us we mistook him for a black leopard! But Manueri found his footprint and no scratch marks on the tree, and there he was, just above us, an ordinary 'kima'. He was one of the big males which grow to a very great size and are often found away from others of their kind. I believe that we were among the first people to observe sexual behaviour in this species, for there are no reports in the literature. One morning in bright sunlight at 8.45 a.m., high up in a tree-top, a female presented to a male which came up, mounted her briefly, then followed her closely and finally groomed her. On two occasions we saw groups of blue monkeys all of which were youngsters, so it looks as if there may be 'age-grades' in this

species. Besides a chirping note similar to the redtail's there is an
alarm call, a distinctive, loud "kyoh!", and another call "ko . . .
ko . . . ko . . . ko . . .", a sort of animated croaking, the function
or meaning of which is completely unknown.

The black and white colobus monkey ('engeye') is our Budongo
showpiece – the film star of the forest, beautifully clad in a robe
of black with a fleecy white mantle around the shoulders and
along the back, and a long black tail with a white tassel at the end.
The colobus is a very distant relative of the redtails and blues,
being in fact closer to the langur monkeys of India than to these
African species. It eats leaves and not fruit, moves about the
treetops by leaping and not running as the others do, has no
thumbs, and possesses the oddest looking face – like a dark
monk peering out of a white cowl with a black skull cap on his
head. Shyer even than the blue monkey, the colobus crashes off
through the canopy with an agility which must be seen to be
believed: it readily leaps anything up to thirty feet from tree to
tree, can run down a tree-trunk *head first*, and members of a group
always follow each other along exactly the same route, hiding
among the shadowy leaves until it is their turn, and then moving
so fast it is hard to see them. When at rest, however, this is a
charming animal, which, if not busily feeding on the tender leaf-
tips of vines and creepers, sits in pairs or threes just dozing side
by side, or, if a youngster is present, putting up with its on-
slaughts as it plays. Once we noticed an adult colobus which
was being pestered in this way switch its tail to and fro just like a
cat. But the most staggering thing about this animal is its call – a
long, deep, vibrating gargle, repeated anything up to fifty times;
it is much more like a frog's croaking and when we first searched
for the source of the noise I remember we had our eyes to the
ground looking for some giant bull-frog. According to Manueri,
the colobus gargles at six in the morning and six in the evening
and quite often this was the case. But it also gargles at other times,
and I can make it do so. There, deep in the forest, I found a use
for a habit I had secretly developed in London, despite all the
strictures of society to the contrary: the habit (approved, I may
say, by the Emperor Claudius) of belching loudly after a meal.
One day, as we sat among the leaves having lunch, swallowing
the last doughy remnants of our squashed bread and chewing

out the last bit of goodness from some very gristly beef, I let rip and was immediately answered by a colobus several hundred yards away. It worked again on other occasions, and I think the explanation may be that the colobus is a territory-minded monkey, and is quick to outdo any gargling in his area with gargling of his own.

Our last monkey is the olive baboon. Dog-faced, noisy, cheeky, curious: we all know baboons. Here in Budongo they are often seen in troops of enormous size, too big to count, for one never sees all the animals. At night they sleep in trees, but by day they wander along the forest floor eating the pithy stems of shrubs, digging up roots, and quarrelling occasionally; they sometimes clamber up into trees to eat the fruits, tumbling out of them with neither poise nor grace as we come along. On the ground they are more confident, peeping through the leaves at us, tossing their heads and stamping their feet as if incensed, while a big male barks ceaselessly at us in a dog-like voice. It is hard to love a baboon unless, I suppose, you are a baboon yourself; but it is easy to laugh at them, especially when Manueri starts talking to them. Putting his hand to his lips, he imitates superbly the noise of a frightened baby baboon – a high-pitched whining, squealing sound – and the response is immediate: the baboons get agitated, they look and look, taking up new vantage points, crowding closer all the time, anxious to see if we have caught a youngster and are holding it by the tail.

*

Unlike their cousins in La Fontaine's fables and so many delightful children's stories, the various species of animals in the Budongo Forest kept rather aloof from one another, coming together, as in the case of the monkeys and birds and butterflies to feed on a common food, but otherwise moving around alone or with others of their own kind. Perhaps some species could recognize the alarm calls of other species. For example, on one occasion we were quietly watching a big mother chimpanzee and her 'toto' when from close by there came three loud coughs of a 'swara' (bushbuck) which had probably caught our scent; the mother looked attentively towards the sound, then took her baby below her belly and descended. She had been alone, and anyway mothers are more than usually careful.

But it was food which acted as the magnet bringing different kinds of animals together. Blue monkeys and redtail monkeys, both fruit eaters, were often together or with chimpanzees in the same tree, while the colobus monkeys, with their diet of leaves, were usually out of the party. But the baboons, although they eat fruit, were never seen with groups of these smaller monkeys, because they are a dominant species, so that, when they arrived with their noisy screeching and bullying manner, the other monkeys scampered away. And here it was interesting for us to note that the chimpanzees, while so much stronger than the baboons, would mix and feed with the smaller monkeys but would move a short way off, in a dignified manner, when the baboons arrived, as if they found their company distasteful. Thus, our chimpanzees left a tolerance-radius of one tree-span between themselves and baboons, but they allowed individual redtails to come as close as five yards and blue monkeys as close as three yards to them; then, however, their patience was exhausted, and with a little threatening jerk they chased the cheeky monkey away. And some of the monkeys, especially the redtails, were cheeky. They would run along a branch where an unsuspecting chimpanzee sat feeding and jump right over him, or zip under his nose as fast as they could, but we never saw a chimpanzee get angry to the point of chasing a monkey; it was beneath his dignity, one felt, not worth the effort; and anyway it would be doomed to failure in the end as the featherweight monkey leapt along little branches which would send a chimpanzee crashing to the ground. With blue monkeys we saw something which had been reported in the past: a single large apparently male monkey moving around with a group of chimpanzees. We saw this on several occasions, always in the trees, and could never establish for sure whether, when the chimps moved off along the ground on one of their tracks, the 'kima' moved along with them or kept up above them in the trees. Perhaps he didn't travel with them at all. For lone males are known in many species of monkeys, and it is quite possible that, attracted by the calls of the chimpanzees (which he knows from experience to mean that food is abundant), and knowing that the big black apes will tolerate him in the tree with them, he turns up and starts feeding with them, and that is where we find him. More evidence is needed before we can say that he moves with them from place to place.

Apart from these monkeys, the chimpanzees have little contact with other species except that they are continually bumping into them as they move about the forest. With their silent tread they must often come up against duikers, they must see snakes from time to time, birds are never far away in the treetops, ants they eat occasionally. Leopards, we think, do not bother them, preferring tastier morsels. Their response to elephants and buffaloes we never could determine.

Sometimes they run into an unfortunate animal caught in a snare, and Manueri had a fascinating story to tell of this. I had been discussing with him the question of whether the Budongo chimpanzees ever ate meat. He denied this emphatically and related as follows. One day four years ago he had set a snare to catch a duiker. On returning to it he saw that it had been interfered with – by men, he thought. As he was leaving in disappointment, he heard a noise in the trees and, looking up, saw a chimpanzee holding a dead duiker in its arms and tossing it up and down. Manueri went away and returned the following day; the 'nende' had fallen to the bottom of the tree, it had not been bitten into; he himself ate it that evening. Coming from a stranger I would have passed this off as a bit of fanciful story-telling, but from Manueri I believed it. We had often watched duikers picking their dainty way beneath a group of feeding chimpanzees, which never took any interest in them. But a struggling, snared duiker might be well expected to arouse their curiosity; perhaps a whole band, running into the victim, had gathered excitedly around, hooting and thumping, maybe even pulling at the duiker and finally breaking its neck. One of the more curious of them, not wanting to part with such a prize, could have pulled it out of the snare and dragged it up the tree, given it a thorough examination and then dropped it.

Who knows? The forest is full of surprises.

CHAPTER FIVE

Days and Nights

Just as the equatorial sun starts and ends his day with a grand regularity, so on our own smaller scale we imposed a pattern on our days to fit in with the sun. Our morning routine was especially impressive. It went like this: at six o'clock Semei's alarm clock (which we had loaned him) rang (if it was wound up). He then (if he heard it) went down to the outside kitchen and loaded the Dover stove with 'kuni' – bits of firewood – which, when dashed, soused, or flooded with paraffin (depending on how damp the wood was) usually caught fire. By 6.30 Frankie and I were up. It was now beginning to grow light enough to see. Dressing quickly, and fixing her make-up by candle-light with a tiny piece of shattered mirror, Frankie went backstage to supervise the breakfast while I cleaned my teeth thoroughly, a thing I enjoy doing very much and which does not suffer from using boiled water. I then made my way to the verandah which was the one and only place to be at dawn. There I pottered about, cleaning binoculars and checking films, taking temperature readings with a whirling cyclometer (before I broke it), and listening all the while for early chimpanzee calls from the forest.

By a quarter to seven, all being well, huge mugs full of friendly steaming tea appeared; we swallowed down our anti-malarial 'Paludrine' pills and started on the bacon, which, however charred, had that special flavour without which no Englishman can honestly face the day. On top of this we had toast – Frankie made the bread, and we had brought with us a little square grid, bought in Woolworths, which made excellent toast – and marmalade. These dawn breakfasts on the verandah were our greatest luxury. The cool morning air gave us hunger, and as it grew light and the mist-furrowed forest could be seen below we wondered idly what the day would bring. At seven the sun appeared redly just opposite us over the forest. It was the moment to leave. I called "Manueri!" and heard the muffled answer from his hut "Bwana!" In an instant he was with us, panga in hand, and, after saying "Jambo" and sharing out the load we headed down the steps to start the day.

The load varied from day to day. Our basic necessities were compasses, binoculars, and the lunch bag, which also contained our plastic macs, caladryl (anti-itch) cream, maps, knife, note-book, pencil, and the Fitzsimons Anti-Snake Bite Kit. Lunch consisted of a beef sandwich each and a small bottle of boiled water. It was no use taking more: bulk and weight were our enemies, on top of which the meat was tough and tasteless and the bread doughy. Apart from these basics, I sometimes took either the still camera or the cine or the tape recorder (until it went wrong). These latter two were heavy items and when I did take them Manueri and I took turns at carrying them. The biggest nuisance of all was the heavy tripod I required with the cine, which, however it was carried, managed to get itself tangled with every hanging liana and vine we passed. Thus, most of the time these heavy items stayed at home.

Depending on how far we were going along the road, we either took the Land-Rover or set off on foot, but most days the chimpanzees were not close by. If we knew where to find them from the previous evening, well and good; otherwise we had to start by visiting 'listening points' along the edge of the forest and inside it along the tracks. We drove a half mile, then stopped, got out, and sat down to listen, for ten or fifteen minutes at each point. There was nothing we could do about this waste of time; if we had no idea where the chimpanzees were, we just had to wait for them to announce themselves. We had some very frustrating days, quite a number of them, when we sat about all morning looking glum, as the forest warmed up around us and our chances of hearing anything grew slimmer and slimmer, for chimpanzees are noisier and their calls carry further in the early morning than later on. But most days our perseverance was rewarded, and we would hear the faint familiar sound through the trees. I would check with Manueri – "Soko-mutu?", and he would say "Iko" – "Here", pointing with finger or lips, and we would decide whether they were 'karibu', 'karibu kidogo', 'mbale kidogo', 'mbale' or 'mbale sana', – 'near', 'a little near', 'a little far', 'far', or 'very far', while I took a compass bearing.

Then, with an inevitability which had a strange pleasure for us, we began the long trek that might or might not lead us to the chimps.

Manueri went first, I second, and Frankie third; it was always the same. Once or twice when Manueri disagreed with the compass I took the lead. It happened like this. We might have been following a moving band of chimpanzees round in a circular path until we were in fact facing the opposite way from the way we had come in. Or we might have taken a zig-zag path through the forest following first one band and then another and then a third. Sooner or later we would decide to abandon the chase and return home. During the day Frankie would keep a track of every bearing we followed and the approximate distance we covered on that bearing. This she drew on a page in our note-book, and at the end of the day we had a fair idea which direction would take us back to our starting point. Manueri, on the other hand, had only his innate sense of direction to rely on, and, while it was better than ours, it was decidedly fallible. So when the moment of truth arrived, and with a confident gesture I held out my arm in the direction of home and said, "Let's return," Manueri would head off in a different direction with equal confidence and expect us to follow him. On these occasions a maximum of tact was necessary, and I had also to bear in mind that we might, just conceivably, have used the compass wrongly. Manueri had spent fourteen years wandering in that forest, and although he could still get completely lost in it, he considered this impossible and an outrageous suggestion. So the conversation went something like this:

"Wait a little. We want to go there," I say, pointing.

"No," he replies, shaking his head vigorously. "That way will take us deep into the forest, we want to return to the Land-Rover. The Land-Rover is here," pointing to where he thinks it is.

"No, that way is the big forest. The road is here." I follow the line of the compass needle with my arm.

"No. You go that way. I'm going back to the Land-Rover. I know the forest."

"Yes, I know you know the forest. However, it is not me who knows you are wrong, it is the compass. Compass says: this way."

Shelving all responsibility on to the little black box in my hand. Very neat.

But the first few times it didn't work at all. "Compass rongo," he asserted, and it was absolutely impossible to shift him. So, the first few times, before I learnt better, we followed him on his chosen route, against all the dictates of compass and map, until, exhausted, and his confidence weakened, he was beginning to doubt the wisdom of going on along a route which should have brought us to our track hours ago. Choosing my moment with some care I would say, "Manueri, you are taking us deep into the forest. Follow me," and turning about, Frankie following, without another look at him, we walked away. Argument was futile in these cases, for Manueri just lost dignity as he racked his brain for reasons to justify his direction, which even he himself no longer believed in. As time went on his respect for the compass grew and he thought carefully before arguing with it. "Compass knows, it knows very well," he said, and, entering into the spirit of this new navigational aid, he would even stop from time to time and ask, "Here, or here?" It was a great victory for modern science.

The fear which dominates all others in the forest is the fear of getting lost. Manueri told us the following story. It was in the days when he was working for the Forest Department, and he would go out every day with his fellow workmen, deep into the forest to tend the trees. I wish I could tell the story in his own words, with the expressions of his face and pauses for effect. The men were walking through the trees when suddenly they spotted a creature sitting at the foot of a big tree, it was like a man only deathly thin, crouched up, with the skin clinging to the bones, and big dark eyes which gazed steadily out at the approaching men. "Eeee! Ahh!" they exclaimed, pointing; and then they ran as hard as they could back to the work camp. It was "Satani ya kibrani" – "the devil of the forest," a being which is terribly dangerous to meet. They told their story to the Forest Ranger, an educated man, who decided to investigate. Reaching the spot, the Ranger announced to the cowering men: "This is no devil, this is so-and-so, the man who got lost three months ago." It was, indeed, one of an earlier working party who had got lost in the forest and had been given up for dead. They lifted him up, he was light as a feather, his legs and arms were stiff and would not move, and yet he was alive. They took him to the hospital and he recovered and is now working at the mill. It was a miracle he had not been eaten by a leopard or, worse, by ants.

I do not know how many victims the forest claims every year; probably not many, for men go into the forest in pairs or groups and very rarely alone; and women go in very rarely indeed. People are said to get lost most frequently when going for elephant meat after a kill: they decide to take a short cut and are not heard of again. But these local Africans, for the most part, leave the forest well alone and it is only the desire for meat which takes them into it.

Sometimes as we walked through the forest we used to imagine what it must be like to be lost, perhaps in order to prepare ourselves for that eventuality. I remember a conversation with Manueri on the subject.

"If we were lost, completely, what would we do?"

"We would go in a line, straight until we got out of the forest."

"And if that did not work?"

"We would look for tracks."

"And if there were no tracks?"

"We would listen for sounds from the road."

"And if there were no sounds?"

"Then we would be lost completely."

"And what would we eat?"

"Ah, man cannot eat the fruit of the chimpanzee. We would eat mushrooms, and I would snare duikers."

"And if you had no wire?"

"Then I would use a creeper."

"And if we could not get food?"

Manueri was not entirely pessimistic and it would be good, I felt, to have him around if we ever did get lost. Take those mushrooms he had mentioned, for instance. We had already found some once before. One day, walking through a glade we knew well, we had been surprised to see the whole of the forest floor covered with a white mantle, which, on examination, turned out to be made up of thousands of tiny white mushrooms, their little heads perched daintily on tall white succulent stems. "Oh – mahoga

muzuri!" – "good mushrooms!" said Manueri, and set to work
collecting them by the handful until our bag was crammed
full. "Mimi tarudi kesho," he said – "I shall return tomorrow,"
and then a thought worried him – "labda nyamagogoto takuja" –
"perhaps tortoises will come" – according to Manueri, these
mushrooms were the favourite diet of the tortoise. Returning
to our theme, however, I doubt whether, without Manueri's
assurance that they were good, we should ever have picked any
of those little mushrooms at all, for fear of agonizing death by
poison; as it was, we all had a wonderful feast that evening.

But, I am glad to say, we never got seriously lost. At times
the situation looked hopeless and we certainly knew the fear
that grips one when, hour after hour, the familiar, long-awaited
track one is heading for fails to show up. One problem was that
our rate of progress was so variable, depending on how thick the
forest was. So that, even though we knew the various bearings
we had followed, and the time spent following each, we never
had any clear idea of how far we had gone on each bearing; in
short, we never knew exactly where we were. I remember one
occasion when we were in the swamp-forest of the Siba, a part
we had hitherto avoided, miserable slushy forest with bilharzia-
ridden streams and spiny rattans everywhere and giant curtains
of cobweb hanging like closely woven muslin from the trees. In
that gigantic swamp the trees themselves were covered in great
spikes, sticking out like daggers all around the trunk. Why any
tree should need such massive armaments I could not imagine –
was there a time when giant beasts waded through these swamps,
curling their tongues around every sapling which did not resist?
Or perhaps it was elephant protection. There certainly were
elephants in this part of the forest, for their heavy tracks were
abundant. Tree ants in millions lived in the swampy undergrowth,
and fell on us in black showers whenever we cut through a thick
patch of rattan and shook them off their arboreal highways. They
fell down our necks and got tangled in our hair, and each little
devil bit until it was killed. Their nests hung like big black foot-
balls in the bushes. We stopped in a glade to rest, the chimpanzees
were on the move and leading us a merry dance through the
swamps. They called ahead quite close and we moved on. The
day was hot and the swamp less cool than true forest, as the

canopy was thinner. We got close to the chimpanzees but they eluded us, we dodged this way and that, determined to close the gap between us. The ants by now were driving us mad, and our legs were soaked in vile swamp water which we knew would bring our skin up in blisters. Manueri was as tired as we were. We sat down to have lunch and rest. No sooner had we taken the first bite than there was a movement on the ground ahead of us and a knocking of branches. We listened carefully. We had never heard this noise before. Manueri whispered, "Hi tembo," – "that's elephant," we looked at him incredulously. If it was true it was bad, and we did not intend to establish whether it was true or not. Packing our half-eaten lunch, we silently melted away in the direction of home. Settling down again half a mile away, Manueri beat a tree with the side of the blade of his panga: the noise rang out like a rifle shot, and in the distance we heard animals crashing through the trees. It was a trick he had learned for scaring them, but one that could only be used at a safe distance.

After lunch we went on, and it was then that we realized the extent of our troubles. For walking along our homeward bearing we suddenly came to the edge of the forest, an ocean of elephant grass where nothing but forest should have been. On the far side of the grass the forest began again. We had to decide whether to cross the grass or go around the edge in the swamp. The compass pointed resolutely across the grass. Manueri pointed another way which I felt sure was wrong. I hated that swamp, hated the gnawing feeling that I was being impregnated with worms at every sodden footfall even more than the rattan splinters and the ants.

"I know where the Land-Rover is," I said, perhaps to convince myself. "It is over there. We shall cross the grass. Follow me." It was a decision born of ignorance, fear, and ill-temper. The sheer misery of crossing that field of grass was my reward. Every step had to be prepared, by pushing down the wall of grass which rose fifteen feet ahead of me. Cutting it with the panga was futile, there was simply too much. And pushing it down meant that with every push my fingers and knuckles were filled with fine prickles from the grass, which quickly became sores. And the heat outside the forest was so intense that after a hundred yards, with the distant trees not a whit nearer, the sweat was

9*a*. Blue monkey.

9*b*. Redtail monkey.

10*a*. A male picking insects off a tree.

10*b*. A chimpanzee's nest on the ground.

pouring off me and blinding my eyes. There were ants in the grass too. Suddenly I pushed down the wall ahead and was surprised to find the way ahead for ten yards or so already prepared – it looked as if a steam roller had been over the ground. "Nyati," said Manueri, in his blasé style for use on occasions of tension – "Buffalo." I shrugged and went on. Now every time I pressed at the wall I expected to hear a snort and see a great black sleeping form rise up and greet me with a toss of horns. Half-way across the grass I almost fell over with exhaustion and fear.

Without a word, Manueri came forward and began to tackle the grass. As always, he had a better way of doing it – with his left arm he pulled the grass over sideways and with a cut from the panga made a thin channel for us to walk through. We finished the journey in due course, and sank back into the cool forest with relief. Now I no longer challenged Manueri's leadership – this had been his victory and he was in charge. We were completely lost, and our bearings too, and we were too weary to care. He led us along a river, for miles it seemed, and suddenly we came across a woman washing clothes, her naked children clinging to her dark green dress in fear as they peeped at us, at our bedraggled hair, our bleeding hands wrapped around in handkerchiefs, and our backs wet with sweat. We sat down and Manueri talked to her. Above us redtail monkeys chirped and groomed each other, and from near by we heard the sound of people. We had lost our way alright, but thank God we had run into a village. Manueri sat still, perfectly composed, talking as if he had just got up after a good afternoon's rest.

"Where are we?" I said. "Do you know this place?"

"I know it," he replied. "This is where I used to live."

*

At the end of the day's work in the forest a new routine comes into play. Dragging ourselves wearily up the forty-odd steps to our house, we drop on to chairs exhausted while Semei fixes us a well-earned mug of tea. After this, and revived by an all-over wash in cold water and a complete change of clothes, I settle down to copy our field notes from the pocket book into our big chimpanzee log, a job which often takes a couple of hours; also

I

any leaf or fruit samples collected during the day have to be pressed or bottled. As dusk falls, the Tilley is lit and I work on by its hot hissing radiance, among a bombardment of 'dudus' from the forest night, while delicious smells of stew waft through from the kitchen and find me on the verandah. Generally we sup by candle-light as it is less hot than the Tilley, and fewer insects get into the food. Meanwhile hyraxes call from the trees below and a tropical moon, wisped over now and then by slow moving clouds, gazes down at our humble spread. We open a bottle of beer and sip it lovingly, revelling in the soft cool of the night wind as it brushes our bare arms and necks. Most evenings, some late calls of chimps come to our ears.

We talk of anything; but often we try to compare this strange life of ours with that dimly-remembered one we led in London, to which, we know with certainty, we are fated to return. We ask ourselves: what is it that makes the contentment we feel, living out here in the African bush? The climate is harder to bear than it was at home, with its continuous succession of humid hot days that sap your strength. We work longer hours here, from dawn to dusk most days; despite the fact that we eat enough we are both steadily losing weight and our clothes hang about us. We aren't masochists though, or never used to be – so why do we like this life?

Perhaps it is because we are not hemmed about by doubts and guilts. If you get up at dawn, there is no self-recrimination about starting the day late, wasting valuable time. In London, every day for years, we started almost each day with the feeling we were in a hurry, late. This is not to advocate that everyone in London should get up at dawn, but simply to state that getting up at dawn is more satisfying than getting up at any other time. For there was definitely a time in our ancestry when our fore-fathers lived the same daily cycle as the monkeys and chimpanzees do now, waking at dawn and going to sleep at dusk; and this rhythm is inherent in us and satisfying to perform. Man seems, however, to have reached a stage where eight hours of sleep are sufficient, while the monkeys and chimpanzees in our forest sleep for twelve. Thus man can and does stay awake and active for four hours after dusk here on the equator. How he has achieved this is unknown – perhaps he finds and grows foods of greater nutritive value during the daylight hours than the vegetable diet of the gathering monkeys, thus enabling him to remain active for longer and reduce the period of energy-conserving sleep. At all events the guilt-feelings resulting from getting up late are not paralleled at the end of the day – going to bed at dusk after twelve waking hours leads to no satisfaction, while staying awake, sitting around the fire or Tilley lamp, drinking and talking in the warm black night air, is one of the pleasantest experiences we know.

Doubt, too, is lacking from our life out here. Not just petty doubts, about whether to take the bus or the tube for example, but doubts about the meaning of life, the wisdom of staying in one's particular job. Here these problems do not exist; we are too involved in the work and the business of living to give the matter a thought. For there is no possibility of changing jobs – quite apart from our obligations to the University, there isn't another job in Uganda we would rather do. How different it is in London, where there are always other jobs which seem to offer just that little more sparkle and remuneration than one's own. As to the meaning of life, we have not solved that one, but we are holding it at bay, too engrossed in living to think about it. At home, life did not hold us so firmly in its grip and so our minds were more detached and philosophical. Here we do not ponder deep matters: we ponder the social life of chimpanzees, the toughness of the meat, the tick which has buried itself in our groin.

It is a fact that our life in Africa is a good deal more real and purer than life in the big city. That world, at home, was composed totally of make-believe: we talked about television, plays, films, books, 'famous' people, and so on. So insulated were we from dangers that, like the captive raccoon which 'washes' his food in his water bowl because in the wild he would catch it in a stream, we sought them out on the X-certificate screen or in the mad speed of the big dipper. And when reality struck: death to a near one, an accident or illness to ourselves, we were bowled over, it was hard or impossible to comprehend. In Africa death and disease and accident are never far away. We take our anti-malarial pills each morning, but against such diseases as bilharzia we have no protection except a little knowledge. One day or another, each of us meets his snake, or an elephant on the road; we hear the leopard's coughing grunt in the forest, we feel the pinch when food stocks fail to arrive, we fall ill. Our lives, like those of all other animal species, lack guilts and doubts but are closely circumscribed by fear.

But we are tired and the heavy scents of the flower trees in the garden make us drowsy. Shutting the door behind us, we grope our way through to our stone bedroom and within minutes are in our sleeping bags on deliciously comfy Safari camp-beds, fast asleep.

*

For some time we had had the idea of spending a week or so inside the forest by night instead of by day. The advantage of this was that we would be able to watch the chimpanzees making their nests, and be in position again next morning to watch them getting up; we had found this difficult up to now as we generally had to leave the chimps before they made their nests in order to be out of the forest by dusk, and the difficulties of getting into the forest before dawn without making any noise had defeated us. The game warden at Masindi, John Heppes, had authorized us to take along the two local game guards with us, Okenyi and Okello; it was simply a matter of giving them the word.

One day we felt in need of a change from our routine, and so I went down the road that evening to Okenyi's home and discussed the matter with him. He agreed to start next day; I told him we should leave at four p.m. I would locate some chimpanzees during the early afternoon, and we would try to intercept them later and follow them to their sleeping place. Frankie set to work preparing the rucksacks.

When we set off there were seven of us: the game guards and their porters, us two, and Manueri; we looked like a guerrilla patrol, dressed in khaki, bristling with arms, walking in single file and without speech through the forest. I had found some chimpanzees which now called in the distance, and we made a beeline for them. Manueri went first, followed by the guards, myself, and Frankie, with the porters bringing up the rear. We moved along as silently as seven people can, but still I felt we were making as much noise as a bull elephant. Our months of tracking had made us noise conscious; we knew how to step over twigs that might snap and could tell when a twig was damp and would not crack but just disintegrate, and we knew also that every so often one accidentally makes a noise. Now our numbers were doubled and we each had a pack on our backs and the net result was a constant succession of nerve-racking snaps and crackles.

The afternoon was hot after the rain, streams flowed along the valleys we crossed, and as each man reached the water he bent down and scooped a handful to his mouth and drank it, then another, and wet his sweating face and neck with a third. We two did not touch the water if we could help it, for, rightly or wrongly, we did not trust it. We knew that our pampered civilized bodies reacted violently to things which the local Africans took in their stride, malaria for instance, or dysentery. Their systems had become tough and resistant through constant infection and re-infection. If they had not, these men would have sickened or even died as children, the natural fate of many of Africa's sons and daughters, which checks her population growth despite the high birth rate.

As we approached the chimpanzees which seemed fortunately to be settled and not on the move, I looked around for somewhere to camp. It was essential that we should stop short of them and not disturb them; they would literally run a mile at the sight of this expeditionary force. Finally, in a natural glade with a troop of colobus monkeys gargling beside us, we came to a halt and put down our burdens. We lit cigarettes and chatted in low voices. The plan was to wait until about an hour before dusk and then, if the chimpanzees were still in position, to put up our tents and hammocks on the safe assumption that they would not move far before sleeping. So at 5.30, when they could still be heard close ahead, we arranged our gear. The men quickly had their tents up, but we had a little trouble with our hammocks, which, owing to our lack of experience and the irregular spacing of the trees, never seemed to be quite right. Finally we got them lashed up side by side about three feet off the ground, and I demonstrated my faith in my carefully constructed non-give knots by climbing rather gingerly into each hammock in turn and bouncing up and down in it. Leaving Frankie to put the finishing touches to our arboreal beds, Manueri and I set off towards the chimps.

It was a painfully slow walk as we simply had to avoid any risk of disturbing them. Every tree was given a notch with the panga, and after every few steps we stopped and peered into the trees ahead. We soon found them, and took up positions behind large trees to watch them build their nests. This proved un-expectedly difficult. For a start, it was only possible to watch one chimpanzee, the nearest one, as we did not want to manoeuvre about in search of a good position from which we could see several chimps, but from which we might later not be able to find our way back in the dark to our track and to camp. However, we did get a good view of the nest-building process, and stayed watching until just the odd hand and arm could be seen over the rim of the nest making little adjustments, and the chimpanzees nearby were giving their final hoots and calls for the day. Perhaps they were locating each other, or simply responding to the pleasant bedtime feeling; there was nothing harsh or shrill about these late calls, they were most musical.

Suddenly Manueri and I realized it had grown very dark on the forest floor. Looking up towards the treetops had deceived us, down below all was inky black. We started the homeward trip and almost immediately got lost. Our little white marks on the trees would have had to be luminous to help us. We floundered about, as silently as we could, thinking silent curses as we tripped on lianas. At last we heard a cough from ahead, it sounded human, in fact it sounded rather like Okenyi. We crept forward towards the sound, feeling our way and bumping into each other. A little flicker of light reached us through the trees; in a moment we were sitting round the oil-lamp, relieved at not having got stupidly lost a hundred yards from camp. Vigorously we tucked into our sandwiches. A final cigarette was smoked. Frankie informed me that the site I had selected for pitching camp was beside a huge dead tree; we inspected it and prayed for a calm night.

After that we all went to bed. The Africans went to sleep instantly; we were still shifting about in our hammocks, which insisted on hanging at an angle, ready to pitch us out to the

right or the left the moment we stirred in our sleep. Perhaps
it was the way we had hung them. Finally we decided to lump it.
We lay back trustingly, keeping as still as we could. It was night,
the pitch black night of the forest. We did not know whether
there was a moon in the sky, or whether the stars were twinkling
brilliantly above; everything was blotted out.

From the tent where our protectors lay came irregular snores.
I think we had imagined that the guards would take it in turns
to stay awake, rifle at the ready, poking a dying fire every now
and then and making it flare up again. I think we had imagined a
mutter of voices all night long, and the glimmer of dark bodies
around the fireside. No such luck! The fire was out; the guards
were safely tucked up inside their splendid Game Department
tent and Manueri was in his. We alone were exposed for any
passing beast to take a sniff and a nibble at. Were we afraid?

Oddly enough, not at all. There were noises around us, of tree
hyraxes and owls, and some strange ghostly sounds and some
squeaking, but no terrifying roars or growls. We quickly went to
sleep; we were comforted by the regular peaceful snores of the
guards. Several times in the night the chimps called out loudly and
woke us up; once I awoke to find a creature snuffling about in our
bags below the hammocks – it might have been a duiker or a pig,
a civet or a porcupine, there was no way of knowing. But I felt
no fear – rather I felt a certain intimacy with this creature just
below me. I do not know why, but the thought that it might,
just conceivably, be a leopard never entered my drowsy mind.

Towards dawn a wind got up, and we thought of the tall dead
giant standing on the edge of our camp site. Had destiny arranged
a meeting between us? It would have been a complete disaster for
us if that tree had fallen, and we almost deserved it for our
stupidity. But though the wind blew hard and shrill in the treetops nothing fell, not even a branch, and our fears were relieved.
With the wind came a little rain and we pulled plastic macs over
our bodies, leaving our faces to get wet. We had not needed our
mosquito netting – not a 'dudu' had bothered us all night. At six
the alarm clock in my pocket went off; we staggered out of 'bed'
and roused our companions, who emerged sleepily and in a fairly
good humour. Groping about for our immediate needs – binoculars and so on – in the exact places where they had been

thoughtfully placed the night before but no longer were, we finally got ourselves ready to leave. We were glad to notice that sleeping in hammocks had left our bodies supple, in sharp contrast to the bruised, stiff feeling one has after sleeping on the ground. We looked at the sky which was beginning to lighten through the treetops. No one spoke. Okello wound the khaki puttees around his legs. He still had one leg to do but we could not wait – he could catch us up. Manueri announced that he could now see, and without more ado we set off towards our first white mark.

The new method brought its rewards. In position at last, we scrutinized the tops of the saplings where we knew the chimpanzee was sleeping. Each of us was well concealed behind a big tree. For minutes nothing happened and we thought the chimp might have heard us the night before and hurried off in a panic to nest elsewhere. Then, unexpectedly from one side, came a first hoot, a greeting to the day, followed by a tree-top cough, discreet, rather out of place at that time of day – more like the evening coughs which are heard between movements of a symphony on the B.B.C. After a pause, another hoot, this time joined by calls from several other animals around us. We gazed intently at our nest as the forest grew dimly lighter, still before sunrise. From time to time there was more calling, and we heard the breaking of a branch where a chimp had started feeding to our left. Suddenly I saw Manueri pointing, and there was our chimp, squatting over the edge of his nest for his early morning toilet requirements. Having done this, he clambered speedily down his tree, without a hoot or a look at his abandoned bed, and made off along the forest floor towards the feeding area. No ceremony, no dawdling; having slept the best part of twelve hours, he had woken hungry and hurried off for breakfast.

And what a sight greeted us on the breakfast tree! We edged up slowly to a point where we could see, and found about a dozen chimps, males, females, and youngsters, feeding with tremendous zest on the wild fruits of an 'Ngrube' in the under-storey. They were stuffing handfuls of food into their mouths, looking around all the time for a new bunch, swinging about, and even squabbling to get at the ripest, yellowest fruit. Everywhere chimps were moving about, feeding and hooting and occasionally squabbling, with wild screams from the loser of the fray. This first hour certainly seemed to be the most active feeding period of their day.

We watched for a while, until we too began feeling desperately hungry. The sun was now well up and the treetops were yellow-green. Looking at the guards, I saw that they had tired of watching and were lying on their backs, smoking, while Manueri sat, as he liked to in the forest, in the crotch between two buttesses of a giant tree. They smiled at us, tolerant of our excessive interest in the 'soko-mutu'; but they understood by now that there was nothing in particular we were trying to do, or see, but that we wanted to find out everything about these strange men of the woods, and they were more than pleased when our luck was good and our notebook crammed with information.

We returned to camp where a fire was going, fed on sandwiches and tea, and agreed it had been a good morning. The chimps were far away by now, out of earshot. We packed our bags and trudged out of the forest, getting to the Land-Rover only to find it had a flat tyre. The wheel nuts had rusted on and would not budge; it was uncomfortably hot and the horseflies were biting. There was nothing to do but walk home and walk home we did, arriving at midday with sweat pouring from our faces and darkening our jackets. Tit for tat: we had been favoured for a few hours, and then while our spirits were high we had been damned. We now felt, in the midday heat, that Africa was un-friendly and against us and useless to struggle against – we had walked three miles or more with rucksacks on our backs and cameras and things banging against us.

But we had arranged, despite ourselves, to leave again at five p.m. After a bath and some lunch I walked back to the Land-Rover, lightly clad and armed with a heavy spanner, changed the wheel, and set out looking for a likely group of chimps. The cycle began again.

We kept it up for almost a week, a memorable time in which we gained greater intimacy with the forest and the chimpanzees, got to know the men, and discovered, not only how to hang a hammock, but also how the chimpanzee has solved its sleeping problems. The first of these is knowing just when to start thinking seriously of going to bed. There are several signs: the air cools suddenly, cicadas begin their chirping one by one until the air is a merry din, and hornbills wing their rasping way to their roosting trees outside the forest on the slopes of Busingiro or Little Kasenene hill. All these are indicators of approaching night.

During the last hour or so of daylight, we watched the chimpanzees as they fed briskly, conscious perhaps of the need to have a full stomach on retiring in order to avoid insatiable pangs of hunger at night. Sometimes they looked over the canopy towards the sun, as if to see how the time was running out. Then it flipped behind the hills and, one by one, they left feeding with a last crammed mouthful and made their way out along the branches into another tree, or down the trunk and along the ground.

Then there was some hooting in the still of the evening, as chimpanzees located themselves in their nesting positions, for usually they nested in small groups of three or four, each in sight of the others. Some were already at work, others were selecting a site; a late one was still feeding – perhaps he would not make a nest at all. Site selection was fascinating to watch: one chimp looked up into a sapling, climbed it, climbed down again, went up a bigger tree and out along a branch, and there decided to build. Sitting on the main branch, he pulled in surrounding leafy branches, working his way round in a circle and intertwining the branches, holding them in place beneath his feet. He did not break them off completely but just snapped them half through so that their resilience was gone but they were still firmly attached to the tree. After he had used every available branch at the site, his nest was still patchy, so he collected more branches from near by, breaking them off this time, and laid them on top, or wove them in a little, finally adding leafy twiglets to complete the big, firm structure in which he was going to sleep. He did all this in three or four minutes. Now followed a settling-down period of from five to ten minutes during which he made final adjustments (from our hidden vantage point below, all we could see were vague arms and hands protruding from the rim of the nest and then disappearing into it again), once he called out and was answered by a brief chorus of good-night hoots, musical and melodious, then it was pitch dark and all was still; we stole away to our camp, pretending to be a firefly with our little torch.

Although the nineteenth-century explorer Paul du Chaillu

claimed for himself the distinction of being the first to discover
that some chimpanzees made nests, the fact that the African apes
made constructions of some sort had been reported long before.
Battell, whose account was published in 1613, had said, "They
sleepe in the trees, and build shelters for the raine," but whether
he was writing of the chimpanzee or the gorilla is uncertain.
Du Chaillu's later experience seems to have excited him greatly:

'As I was trudging along . . . I happened to look up at a high
tree which we were passing, and saw a most singular looking
shelter built in its branches. I . . . was told, to my surprise, that
this very ingenious nest was built by the *nshiego mbouvé*. . . . I at
once saw that I was on the trail of an animal till now unknown to
the civilized world. . . . I no longer felt tired, but pushed on with
renewed ardour and with increased caution, determined not to
rest till I had killed this nest-building ape.'

He got one all right, naming it '*Troglodytes calvus*', the bald chimpanzee, one of the two new chimpanzee species he thought he had
discovered. (He was wrong in this: all his specimens were
members of the one species which was already well known.)

As to the question of why chimpanzees make nests, no very
definite answer is possible. Battell's idea, that the nest would
provide protection from rain, is not wholly erroneous, for
although the ape lies on top of its nest and does not crouch
underneath it, the very fact of being off the ground keeps its
body drier than it would be curled up on the soggy forest floor.
But chimps do not need nests to keep them off the ground – they
could just sit in the trees. Alas, we cannot ask our subjects why
they make their nests, but even if we could they might not know,
for their nest-building behaviour has many of the characteristics
of an instinct. One thing is certain – that this complex activity
must have developed for good reasons. Why should those
chimpanzees which do make a nest have an advantage over
those which do not? One way of tackling the problem is by
comparing chimpanzees with monkeys. Both sleep in the trees
and this doubtless provides some protection from that prowling
nocturnal enemy, the leopard. But monkeys do not make nests:
they generally have 'sitting pads' – bony growths at the buttocks –
which help them keep in position on branches during the night.
Chimpanzees, on the other hand, rarely have these sitting pads

although occasionally they do: it may be that they are losing them on account of their nest-building habit. I would suggest that this changeover from sitting pads to nest-making is a result of increasing size. For while a branch is a big object to a monkey, so that it can find a crotch and wedge itself in securely, this is not so for the much larger chimpanzee who has to keep all hundred pounds of himself balanced in a tree all night. So he has responded by making himself a supporting structure, well-developed today but doubtless, in bygone times, no more than a rudimentary structure of a few supporting sticks.

The two hundred and fifty-nine nests we saw were made at all heights, but the commonest height was thirty feet to forty feet, i.e. fairly low down in the top level of the understorey. There may be several reasons for this: down low there is less wind and thus less danger that the chimpanzee will be rocked out of its nest during a stormy night; the branches are younger and more pliable and thus make a more springy nest (foam rubber has nothing on some of the nests we tested); and it would be almost impossible for a leopard to attack a chimpanzee nesting in a sapling, for two reasons: if it climbed up the slender trunk it would cause such a lot of movement that it would wake up the chimp, and if it sprang down out of a nearby tree the sapling would just bend under the combined weight of the two animals and both would crash to the ground, probably becoming dis-engaged in the process. Whereas if a nest is made on a big branch high up in a tree, as indeed some of them are, all these advantages are lost. Nevertheless some nests are made high up in the tree-tops. Fifteen per cent of the ones we saw were over ninety feet high, some a good hundred and fifty feet high. And the lowest tree nests we saw were ten or twelve feet off the ground.

We had found that nests were made primarily for night-time sleeping, but sometimes we noticed that they were made for a nap during the day. And there were other occasions when nests were used. For instance, when a chimpanzee was badly scared but dared not flee, it looked about for an old nest, or, failing that, made one hurriedly and climbed in, hiding there quietly and completely hidden until the danger was past.

Nests were nearly always in the trees but here again there were exceptions, for, during our eight months in the forest, we found two well-constructed nests on the ground. I remember how we came upon the first one in a little clearing of broad-leaved grasses, near a group of nests high up in the trees (Plate 10*b*). It was so well-made, all of grass, and so well pressed down that I wondered if we had a lone gorilla wandering in our forest. Manueri was of the opinion that it was made by a chimp mother for her natal bed but after we had examined it thoroughly for bloodstains we gave up this idea. We then wondered whether it was an old chimpanzee which could not climb very well, or perhaps one that was sick. The second one was made of shrubs and small branches of nearby saplings, a much rougher affair, dreadfully uncomfortable owing to a snapped-off sapling which stuck up right in the middle of it. It was situated at one end of a small tree-bridge over one of the many streams in the Siba. Could it be that a chimp had arrived at this spot late one evening, been uneasy about crossing the water on the thin branch, and finally bedded down on the spot to wait for dawn? We would never know, of course, but we liked to speculate in this way as we tramped through the trees, or lay, hammock-bound, in the forest night. But such problems could hardly be expected to enter the head of Okenyi, who continued to snore away the hours of darkness. And during the daytime his thoughts naturally turned to bigger game. On the sixth afternoon, when I arrived to collect him, he said that an elephant had been heard in a compartment of the Biiso block, and I saw in his eyes the excitement of the hunt. That was his life, not chimp-watching. He had accompanied us graciously, and now must return to his own work. I wished him luck, he grinned broadly, we shook hands, grasped thumbs and shook hands again. There was no more to say, and we parted.

CHAPTER SIX

The Social Life of Chimpanzees

'One of the most remarkable of all the social habits of the chimpanzee, is the *kanjo*, as it is called in the native tongue. The word . . . implies more the idea of "carnival". It is believed that more than one family takes part in these festivities.' Thus wrote R. L. Garner of these apes in West Africa. He went on to describe how the chimpanzees fashion a drum from damp clay and wait for it to dry. Then 'the chimpanzees assemble by night in great numbers, and then the carnival begins. One or two will beat violently on this dry clay, while others jump up and down in a wild grotesque manner. Some of them utter long, rolling sounds, as if trying to sing. When one tires of beating the drum, another relieves him, and the festivities continue in this fashion for hours.' Unlikely? Certainly. Pure fiction? The story has been used in works of fiction – *Tarzan of the Apes*, for example. And yet it is largely true. Apart from the matter of the drum, this account given nearly seventy years ago describes quite well what we heard and saw six times during our stay in the Budongo Forest, only twice, however, at night.

What is this drum, so often reported, and erroneously thought to be made of clay or to be a hollow tree or log known to or carried about by the chimpanzees? The very name of the chimpanzee in Lunyoro, the local language of our area, is 'Kitera' from the stem 'tera' – which means 'to beat' and 'ki', the impersonal pronoun 'it': the chimpanzee is then: 'it beats'. To a European the sound is remarkably like the 'boom' of a big bass drum, not at all like the rat-a-tat of little drums, only occasionally like the medium-pitched kettle drum. Quite early on in our study we were able to establish without a shred of doubt that the chimpanzees produced this sound by beating with hands or feet on the plank buttresses of Ironwood trees; we later found that some other species were used as well, but the sound, which we could obtain by striking the buttress with the palms of the hands, would not come from all those species of trees which had buttresses, the reason for which I do not know. The best buttresses for drumming, after the 'Nyakahimbe' (Ironwood) tree, are those of the 'Mumule' and 'Mpungu' trees. We found it difficult to observe how the chimps drummed, partly because seeing anything on the forest floor was so difficult, but mainly because if they knew we were close at hand they usually either bolted or crept stealthily away. A few times, though, we caught a glimpse of a chimp thudding against a buttress and heard, from close to, not only the 'boom' but the crack of the wood being struck, the same sound as if a non-reverberating surface had been hit. The actual note produced by the buttress as its surface vibrates is the sound which carries through the trees, not the sharp mechanical whack; its enormous carrying power is a result of the long-wavelength of the very low-pitched note, which has greater penetrating power than notes of higher pitch. Most people will have heard a band playing as it goes away down the road, and will know how much longer it is possible to hear the big bass-drum than any other instrument. The chimpanzee has discovered this principle, and the drumming functions, we believe, to enable contact to be maintained between groups of chimpanzees and even individuals scattered widely over vast tracts of forest where, especially at ground level, but also in the treetops, visual communication is severely restricted, i.e. the chimps just can't see each other. Drum buttresses of the finest kind (and the chimpanzees evidently know this too) occur where a tree throws out two planks parallel to each other and about six to nine inches apart, making a sort of open 'box'. If you beat on the outside of such a drum box a beautiful crisp resounding note results, and we several times found depressions in the ground by box drums, where a chimpanzee had squatted.

So much for the drum itself, but what of the 'carnivals'? Long before Garner was writing, a missionary in Cape Palmas, West Africa, named Thomas Savage was describing to the Boston Natural History Society what he knew of the way of life of chimpanzees. This was in 1844, and he wrote '. . . they occasionally assemble in large numbers in gambols . . . not less than fifty engaged in hooting, screaming and drumming with sticks on old logs.' At a later date, in 1931, Henry Nissen, who made the first

thorough scientific study of chimpanzees in the wild, wrote
'although the cries and drumming presaged no danger to human
listeners . . . their very intensity was sufficient to inspire something akin to excited wonderment . . . When drumming and
vocalizing were close by, my guides and porters sometimes
trembled in spite of themselves.'

Manueri called these carnivals 'ngoma', which means 'drum',
or alternatively 'dance', the two ideas being merged in Swahili.
From the early days at Budongo we were used to hearing wild
chimpanzee noises during the night, terrible howling and screaming, and people said that it must be a leopard attacking the chimps.
We came to consider this unlikely, although the noise might well
have been a display aimed at frightening off a predator. Neither
did we believe that the chimpanzees had come down from their
nests to dance in the moonlight; the idea just wasn't good
'chimp'. So we never solved the riddle of the night noises; and
when we had gone into the forest and slept with the chimpanzees
they had called a few times only, never in a really noisy chorus.

It was at the start of the 'Igeria' season that we suddenly came
face to face with our first daytime 'ngoma'. We were watching a
group of chimpanzees on the fringe of a swampy river in the
Siba and had noticed that a new group was moving in closer
from the north, calling and drumming as it came. There were
about a dozen chimpanzees in our group and perhaps the same
number again suddenly climbed up into the Igeria trees with the
first lot, whereupon *all* of them began the wildest screaming and
hooting, swinging about, running along branches at top speed,
leaping down branch by branch to the ground, climbing up
again, shaking branches wildly, and occasionally coming up close
to each other to meet briefly and part again, stamping on branches
and slapping them, and behind all this confusion a steady under-
current of drumming resounded. I think on this occasion the
performance lasted for fifty-five minutes, but note-taking was
quite impossible – all we could do was stand in awe and say un-
scientific things like "Good heavens, look at that one!" It was at
times like this that we felt things about the chimpanzees which
we had not yet formulated in words.

Was this the 'ngoma', the 'kanjo', the carnival of the chimps?
Manueri said yes. We suspected it was a greeting display when

11*a*. The Budongo Sawmill.

11*b*. A chimpanzee 'drum': the buttresses of an Ironwood tree.

12. Young chimpanzee in a *Maesopsis* tree.

two groups met, although we had watched many utterly un-
eventful meetings between groups of chimpanzees as big as
these, and knew that there must be other reasons for this display.
Could it be that there was a latent hostility between the groups,
which had to be worked off? We didn't know enough about
either lot to say. When the carnival was over, however, they all
seemed to be feeding very peacefully beside each other and they
all moved off in the same direction. Later on we saw or heard
more 'carnivals', one of which lasted all one afternoon and was
on again the next morning (and may have gone on all the intervening night). We found one factor common to them: groups
which had moved closer to each other slowly and noisily over a
long period beforehand got into this wildly excited state when
they finally met. And as time went by and we learnt more about
our chimpanzees, we came to the conclusion that the only times
when carnivals occurred were when groups from two different
regions met and joined, either to feed briefly together or to
stay on a common feeding ground for a few days but finally, with
a last resurgence of carnival antics, and with each chimp apparently deciding to which group he wanted to belong and several
dashing madly between the parting camps, going their separate
ways.

Carnivals apart, the most striking thing about chimpanzee life
was the utter tedium of it. We soon found, when in the evenings
we wrote up the day's observations in our 'chimpanzee log' at
home, that though we were seeing chimps nearly every day, very
little of extreme interest was taking place. We were getting
spoiled and fussy. Now that we had mastered the art of finding
our quarry, watching was no longer enough; we wanted to
probe deeper into the secrets of chimpanzee life.

One of the most fascinating areas of study concerned the
chimpanzees' calls. People sometimes ask, "Do chimpanzees have
a language?" and it is a difficult question to answer. For while it
is certain that they do not have 'words' with precise meanings, it
is equally certain that there exists a very complex system of communication in chimpanzees, the most exceptional feature of which
is the fact that a whole group of chimpanzees will combine time
after time each day to produce a communal din which will
carry up to two miles (the distance, say, from Marble Arch to

K

Westminster Bridge) and which is answered by any other groups in the vicinity.

But, getting down to details, we first had to learn to distinguish between the different sorts of calls that individual chimps made. When feeding together, we noticed that grunts and little gruff barks were very common, low-pitched and so quiet that one hardly noticed them; somewhat more excited were the panting barks – low-pitched sounds followed by a noisy intake of breath – which accompanied movement from one tree to another. Then there was the very distinctive 'waa' bark – the sudden, sharp, grating, repeated noise, given with the mouth half-open and lips tensed, which meant 'danger!' and was nearly always a result of a chimp seeing us and taking fright. Another kind of barking was harsh and shrill, but, unlike the alarm call, was given in choruses, and seemed to result from excitement of some kind.

A completely different sort of call, a series of soft moans, was sometimes all we knew of the presence of a chimpanzee ahead of us on the forest floor; this was a 'worried' sound produced by just one animal which was suspicious but perhaps unwilling to make a loud noise and give itself away. Then there were the hoots – panting hoots and long hoots – the calls which formed the basis of the choruses. These fine, loud, whooping calls started at low pitch and intensity with noisy intakes of breath, and then as the chimps got more and more worked up, they pouted their lips, their calls rising to a shriek and culminating in a burst of drumming before all was quiet and feeding resumed again. Screams and squeals were given by frightened chimpanzees engaged in quarrels with one another, and together with howls, roars, and growls, this made up the spectrum of their conversation.

Naturally, it took time before we could distinguish the various types of call, especially as the same call, coming from different animals, had a different tonal quality each time. Also, quite often, various chimps engaged in different sorts of calls at one and the same time, and it was hard to sort out the resultant medley of voices. We made tape recordings and analysed these in the evenings to try and sort out the more complicated passages, playing them over and over again. And we practised imitating the different calls, but somehow our human voices were too musical, not harsh or windy enough to get the real chimp tone.

We tried calling to the chimps in the forest, but they never replied, even to a grand chorus of panting hoots given at full blast by Frankie, Manueri, and me; we just were not sufficiently 'chimp'. However, we did achieve some success by drumming – at least I think we did – for sometimes they seemed to call back or even drum in reply; but then, of course, we could never be sure they wouldn't have done so anyway.

Despite the amazing variety of their calls, we obtained no evidence that chimpanzees communicated complex ideas to one another. The feeding grunts and gruff barks perhaps expressed a feeling of togetherness, for they were not given by a chimpanzee on its own. The 'waa bark' was an alarm signal, and other animals found out where the source of danger was by looking to see where the first chimp was staring. The hooting calls seemed to be an expression of excitement caused by the presence of plenty of food, and also by the coming together of a large number of chimpanzees. Screams and squeals expressed fear and directed the attention of nearby chimps to any group member who was having some sort of trouble. So it can be seen that each kind of call or intonation expressed some feeling or other within the animal, and had certain effects on other animals. In humans, this level of communication is found in such behaviour as laughter or crying; our use of words which have to be learnt, and are specific to particular cultures, is altogether lacking in chimpanzees. Perhaps differences exist between the vocalisations of chimps in one area and those in another – we do not as yet know. If they do, it will make a fascinating subject for study. But however great or slight they may turn out to be, the fact will remain that in its ability to express ideas to its fellows, the chimpanzee has remained very much at the same stage as has been reached by its fellow apes and by the monkeys; despite its undoubted intelligence and ability to learn, it fails at the test of speech.

It has long been known that the vocal organs of chimpanzees do not differ markedly from those of man, and so the 'failure' of chimpanzees to learn speech has been attributed to some mental inadequacy. This may or may not be so – we do not know. But expert analysis of our recordings, using sonograms made from our tapes, showed that the structure of the sounds chimpanzees produce is in some ways very similar to the structure of human

sounds. For just as humans achieve a variety of effects by varying
the pitch of the voice, so do chimpanzees; in short, intonation is
the key to the differences between one sound and another in both
humans and chimpanzees.

Enough on the subject of calls. For the rest, chimpanzee life
seemed a serious, rather tedious business, concerned with finding
enough of whichever small, astringent fruits happened to be in
season, to fill a stomach the size of a man's, and provide as much
energy each day as that required by a long-distance runner!
For the chimps, even when they could have stayed all day in one
ripe fruit tree, were always moving on to a new feeding place.
Rarely were more than two hours spent on any one tree. We soon
came to know when they were getting ready to move on. Gradually the chimps in the tree became restless. Some swung about for
a few minutes, or stamped their feet on the trunk and gave a few
low hoots, then resumed feeding quietly. Often calls were
coming in from another group feeding up to a mile away. Our
chimps stopped feeding and listened, turning to look in the direction of the calls. Then they answered, and began to move about
in the tree. Then, typically, one made up his mind and hurriedly
descended. At the base of the tree he grasped a sapling and bent
it, swishing it to and fro, before pelting off along a chimp track.
The others in the tree looked down. Another one or two left.
The first to leave now drummed a few hundred yards ahead, and
those left in the tree called in chorus, stuffed a few last fruits in
their mouths, and finally left too.

If the chimps continued to call on the way to, and upon arrival
at, their new place then we were able to re-locate them again in
an hour or so. But often we bashed on for hours, with the chimps
constantly moving farther away, always tantalizingly a few hundred yards away. What happened in these cases was that after a
few hours feeding in the early morning on a fruiting tree, they
were spending many of the middle hours of the day foraging on
the forest floor, among low bushes or in the swamp rattans, or
eating the fleshy stems of the long green succulent plants which
grow wherever enough sunlight peeps through the canopy to
supply their broad leaves. When foraging thus, the groups were
dispersed and often quiet except for occasional soft gruff barks
or squabbling squeals. We could never see through the dark

denseness of undergrowth inside the forest, and in this way many a day came to a disappointing end. But the chimps usually had a routine which they kept up for a number of days at a time, and sure enough, next morning, back they were on the previous day's fruit tree. Sometimes when most had moved off in the mid-morning, an ageing grandad, with greying hair and a bald patch on his lower back, would remain behind, gazing out over his domain. Or on other occasions, one or two mothers with their youngsters stayed in the tree, lazily feeding or just staring, apparently unmoved by the excitement which gripped those about to leave.

But what of the social life, the interactions between one chimp and another? Often we watched a party of chimps for hours before any social interaction took place; they were too busy feeding or just sat looking out over the trees and scratching themselves with long sweeps of the hand across the body. There was no burning desire to get together. And then one of them would make his way in desultory fashion towards another, sit beside it and start grooming, or, to use less jargon, back-scratching it. This was the most usual form of social behaviour, and usually occurred when a small number of chimpanzees had settled down peacefully in a comfortable tree after an intense and satisfying bout of feeding, before the call came to move on to a new place. In the periods when fruit was scarce there was so much moving about from place to place that there seemed little time for such relaxed social activities. But when, in the fig season for example, stomachs were visibly bulging around mid-morning, a general wave of sociability would sweep through the group, and soon the animals would be in little knots grooming each other. As in gorillas and many species of monkeys, the females were the busiest groomers. Several females with their young often huddled together all grooming each other. On one occasion we spent hours watching two females in a tree. One was an adolescent and the other was very, very old – so old that her head was bald, her cheeks sunken, her movements slow and laboured; she may have been over thirty, which is old for a chimp. The young one followed her, slowly, wherever she went, as if devoted to her, and every now and then groomed her. Finally grandma made herself a nest and sank down to rest in it, at which the young one left her to feed on nearby branches.

Adult males occasionally groomed each other, but most often females groomed males. One day we watched a female who was very much in demand. There were four chimps in a tree, one female and three adult males. At first they were just feeding. Then one male came along a branch towards the female and sat down with his back to her, obviously suggesting to her that she might groom him. The female who was thus presented with a back, obligingly scratched it for a while, selecting one little spot and carefully examining every square centimetre of it, parting the hairs, and sometimes removing bits of dirt, loose hairs, or anything else she found there. Meanwhile male number one closed his eyes in drowsy ecstasy – I knew exactly how he felt as Frankie is an expert back-scratcher – but, I wondered, how does a non-talking chimp direct the attention of his partner to that persistent little itch just to the left of the spine a little way below the shoulder-blade? As I wondered, male number one shifted his position drowsily, stretching his neck backwards until the top of his head was presented to the good-natured female. Ah – so he wanted a head scratch now. But just at this moment male number two came down from a branch where he had been feeding, and, approaching the grooming couple, he sat down behind the female and started grooming her. This went on for some time, and then the good-natured female turned round to groom male number two, perhaps knowing full well that this was what he wanted all the time, and his unselfish gesture was just a way of getting her to notice him. Meanwhile male number three was feeding and watching the threesome below him. Suddenly male number three swung down towards the grooming group, which immediately split up, and then we saw that the good-natured female was grooming male number three! Was he a more important customer than the other two?

The peace of the afternoon was eventually broken by calls coming over the trees from a neighbouring group, and all the males became alert and swung off one by one out of the tree. We were amused to watch our good-natured female lie down now, stretched out on the branch on one side, head on hand, shut her eyes and go to sleep; her work for the afternoon was completed.

We found that sexual relationships among wild chimpanzees were casual and easy-going, in contrast with, say, wild baboons, where the most powerful adult male has the right to a female on heat, even though she may mate with other males before and after the peak of her cycle, and also in contrast with chimpanzees living in captivity, which often develop passions and jealousies that do not show themselves in the wild.

With chimpanzees, when the female comes into oestrus, which means she is on heat, and sexually receptive to the male, she swells up behind a glorious pink colour, displaying her private parts with such gusto that we used this end of her, rather than her face, for temporary identification purposes. This happens every five weeks, on average, lasting for about a week at a time. During the rest of her cycle, the female is uninteresting to the male, and presumably not interested in him. I remember Frankie remarking on one occasion that she thought this "one week on, four off" shift system was rather a good way of arranging things.

One day we were lucky enough to watch the whole mating procedure in ideal conditions of observation. A neat, black-haired young female with a big rounded pink bottom, was standing still on a branch, her behind pointing towards an adult male sitting very close by in a tree crotch. The male kept eyeing the female from time to time. Then slowly grasping the branch above, but without really moving his position he mated with her for a few seconds, then sat back and looked around. This was repeated twice more, then the male started grooming the female. All this time a young three-year-old, perhaps the offspring of the female, was watching from a branch above. After a while the male lay down and curled up to sleep in his crotch, but the female wanted his constant attention, and soon he had to rouse himself and groom her again. A few minutes later another suitor moved into the picture, a smaller adult male, obviously attracted by the same female. Male number two now also started grooming the female, so both males were courting her. What happened next was a very delicate piece of manoeuvring. The female moved to present her behind to the second male and he made as if to mount her, but then male number one suddenly *started to groom him*. Male number two sat down again, distracted, and both males now engaged in mutual grooming, ignoring the poor desirous female! However, when she decided to leave the tree, both males followed her, male number one going first. Though we did not

see the end of this story, it seems likely that male number two
would in fact have his chance later, but that for the moment,
male number one was chief consort.

On another occasion we observed jungle love-making, the
receptive female was in a tree with no less than four adult males.
After one finished mating with her, he moved away, and another
moved close to pay his attentions. However, not always was a
female on heat surrounded by a retinue. Once we saw a rosy-
blushing female presenting to a male who was trying to get a
good meal, and every time she closed in he simply walked away.
Perhaps she had never learned that it doesn't pay to be too
backward!

In marked contrast with what goes on when chimps are forced
to live cooped up in small cages, we never saw homosexual or
auto-erotic behaviour in our wild animals.

From the amount of noise the chimps made (twenty or thirty
loud choruses a day were quite common), one would have
thought that they were a very quarrelsome breed, but in fact
quarrels were uncommon. One reason for this could well be that
there was so much *space* in the forest that if one chimp did not
like another he could easily avoid him without coming to blows.
Again we have here a difference from baboon society, where all
members of a troop remain permanently within sight of some of
the others, and the dominant males exert their authority to main-
tain a proper deference to age, and direct the group's movements
over the feeding grounds. Chimpanzee society seemed to have
none of this. Chimps seemed to treat one another more as individuals, and their relationships were perhaps more those of
personal likes and dislikes than is the case in baboons. There
were certainly important, powerful adult males. Thus, in the
example given above of grooming behaviour, two adult males
moved away when a third came to present himself for grooming
to the female. On another occasion, we saw a small, thin adult male
literally fall off a branch on to the one below as a large powerful
adult male came striding along. But the big difference between
chimpanzees and baboons was that in the chimps there were no
permanent groups for the forceful, fully mature males to lead.

This did not mean, however, that they never took over leadership functions temporarily – they very often did. For instance,

when a group had been feeding in a tree, climbing around and up and down and with odd members going and others arriving, it was not until a big male descended the tree and let out a big 'boom-boom' on a buttress that the others *all* decided to go with him and hurriedly left the tree. Once, too, a big male was in the lead of a party of seventeen chimpanzees crossing the main road; after they had crossed he went back to the side they had come from for a minute, then re-crossed and the whole lot went hooting and drumming into the forest. Had he been checking up to see if anyone was still to come, a hesitant chimp, perhaps, too shy to cross the road near where we were standing? And then there was a group of four adult males we came to know quite well, big, confident and often curious, coming towards us in a relaxed and dignified manner for a closer inspection: a kind of royal clan. But mostly it was the opposite – suspicious, shy chimpanzees, that made their way through the forest without leaders and left trees in twos and threes as the mood took them, so that we never knew what to expect. Even mothers and their infants sometimes strayed alone – I remember one occasion when I was sitting well hidden in shrubs beside a chimpanzee track waiting for a call, a mother walked right past me less than a yard away, her infant sitting up jockey style on her back. Another time Manueri went off 'choo', suddenly I heard a shout but left him to sort it out, and when he returned I gathered that he had been quietly performing his function when a mother in a hurry had almost run into him, the baby had fallen off and he had tried to grab it, but being rather immobile with his trousers down had failed and the mother had retrieved it before dashing off. The whole thing had amused him immensely.

I was glad that he had not succeeded in catching the baby. It is fun, no doubt, to have a pet chimp around the house, and we would have had no space problems. The little creature and its mother would have been sad at first, and so would we for them, but we would all have got over it. Time would go by and there would be jolly antics on Busingiro Hill and then? We could not keep a growing chimp in our small London flat. He would have to go away. He probably could not be returned to the forest as he would have grown too attached to humans, and to us in particular; and if we really were determined to set him free this might be a long process, as Barbara Harrisson has discovered with her orang-utans. Almost certainly it could not be done cleanly and quickly at a time determined by our departure. There might be a good home somewhere, but he would go on growing and would reach the stage all too quickly when he didn't know his own strength. Then a steel cage would be found for him, and in it he would spend the whole of his maturity, the whole of these wonderful Budongo years of meetings and explorations and carnivals and stormy nights under the treetops. Too great a sacrifice, surely, for a few months of fun and games? I told Manueri, as I had before, that we wanted no pet chimps.

Just occasionally, two chimps started to quarrel. These were usually short scuffles in which the animals either actually fought or one threatened the other by means of barks and branch-shaking, while the victim screamed long and loud in a high-pitched piercing voice. From the screams alone one would have hought that one of them was being murdered, but it was gener-ally no more than a tiff over a bunch of fruit. When a real fight started in a tree all one could see was a tangled mass of arms and legs struggling together among the leaves, but since both animals had to hang on for dear life with at least one hand their freedom was curtailed, and after a few seconds one dived down on to a lower branch screaming and looking up at the victor with mixed fear and hate in its eyes. Within ten minutes the two of them might be feeding quite happily beside each other again.

Big males rarely came to blows. I remember one morning (it was one of the mornings when we had spent the night in the forest) we were watching a big male *feeding from his nest* – he had sited it beautifully the night before, right among several enormous clusters of lovely ripe yellow 'Ngrube' fruits. So he sat breakfast-ing in bed like a film star and all he needed was a maroon silk dressing gown and a copy of *The Times* brought in by a butler on a silver tray. But, instead, a male of about his own size came up along a branch, reached the nest, pushed him rudely with a hand, at which he resisted, pushed again, and he meekly got up and left it, threatening the newcomer from behind his back with a couple of jerks, and then shambling miserably away.

One day a chimp decided to quarrel with us! It was in June, and we were in the Siba swamp forest, closing in on some chimps, which were about a hundred yards away in the treetops. We were standing near a big tree with a thick liana snaking down from it. Manueri climbed on to a bend in the liana and looked towards the chimps to try and locate them. He jumped down and his feet thumped on the ground. "Wewe sokomutu," I said – "you are a chimp." He laughed. We edged forward and had scarcely gone a couple of paces when we heard movements ahead on the ground. We froze to watch whatever was coming our way. At that moment a big adult male broke cover and came for us in a slight curve. He was a big chimp, his head was sunk deep on his shoulders, his eyes were cast down and his mouth was shut in a scowl. He was galloping silently towards us in leaps and I felt certain he was going to attack. Manueri immediately took a step towards him and slashed about with his panga, hissing. I shouted and raised the camera tripod I was carrying, ready to bring it down on his head. He turned on his tracks and ran back into the bushes out of sight. Later on I was to be charged by an adult male gorilla, and learn how much more terrifying that can be, but this experience with the chimpanzee was a shock; we measured the distance to the spot where he had churned the earth up in his turning – it was three paces from where we had stood.

Two days later, in the very same area, we had another surprise – this time we met a bad-tempered old lady. Once again we were creeping up to a group feeding about seventy yards ahead, where we could hear the rustling of branches and the gruff barks of a party of chimpanzees. There was a noise in the undergrowth close by to our right, and at the same time a chimp baby started screaming a short way up a nearby tree. We turned and suddenly an old female rushed out of cover, with lowered brows and mouth half open, eyes fixed on us, and charged straight towards us. Again we prepared to defend ourselves. The chimp stopped, glowered at us from five yards, then just as suddenly as she had appeared, rushed back, up the tree to collect the toto, and off with it across a tree-bridge over the river Siba and into the trees. This was the only time we knew of when a female behaved in such a way. Perhaps when she saw us she was separated from her baby and wanted to bluff us so as to give herself time to retrieve it. We admired both her courage and the sensible way she had left baby behind when running against the foe. But Manueri shook his head and said, "A-a, if we come here to these wild Siba chimps too often we shall definitely be bitten; *Siba kali sana:* the Siba is very wild." So we left them alone for a couple of weeks. Anyway, we told ourselves, they were a rotten lot of chimps, and they lived in a dismal swamp.

These were two of the very few moments when there was ever any question that a chimp might attack us. With gorillas which, like chimps, are normally harmless creatures unless provoked, the advice, if you are charged, is to stand still and calm, facing the animal, when it will stop. This requires courage – more, as it turned out, than we ourselves had. But with chimps I would not give that advice; I think it is better to step forwards, shout, and threaten back if things get too hot.

CHAPTER SEVEN

Africans of Budongo

If you ask the Department of Lands and Surveys, Uganda, for a
copy of air photo Number 51/UG/6.017 you will see on it a sec-
tion of the southern rim of the Budongo Forest. At first the photograph will strike you as being extremely monotonous, showing as
it does a sea of trees over most of the area, with tentacles of forest
probing out southwards at the bottom. Then your eye will be
drawn to a little bare patch near the centre of the map in the trees,
and looking carefully you will see thread-like lines running to
and from it. This patch is the site of Budongo Sawmills, Ltd.,
the largest sawmill in Uganda, and the threads are, of course,
roads.

Coming down to earth, and standing in the middle of that same
triangle, the picture is very different. For a man is midget-sized
in comparison with the vast area he has cleared and, standing in
the middle of the mill, it is easy to forget completely the surrounding miles of trees. Let us look around more closely. Entering from the south, we pass the labour lines to our left – white,
well-built huts in which the loggers and sawyers live with their
families – and come to the mill 'duka', which sells maize meal,
beans, cigarettes, salt, tea in tiny packets, native cloth, exercise
books and pencils and a variety of other things such as 'Tembo'
coffee, locally grown and two shillings a pound. The duka has a
verandah which is covered with dirty children. Opposite is a
huge timber store, roofed over, with hundreds of planks stacked
neatly in criss-cross pattern to air. Further up is the dispensary –
a local first-aid unit run entirely by the mill for its staff. If this
sounds commonplace, consider that here, totally unsung, is an
outpost akin to that splendid achievement, the National Health
Service, for the men and women who receive treatment here pay
nothing – the dispensary is subsidised by the mill. It is run by a
beaming African who always wears a green sweater – his methods
of treatment vary according to the man in front of him. He knows

147

the lazybones, and his response to people who have not clearly
got some specific disease or injury is generally one of scorn. I
remember one occasion when Manueri appeared on a Monday
morning nursing a very bad leg and swollen knee; fearing a
dislocation I took him to the dispensary where this man gave
him a whack on the back and told him to drink less 'warigi' then
he wouldn't fall over. It was the best thing he could have done
and Manueri was soon perfectly all right again. Had the dis-
penser sympathised and felt the tender knee and bandaged it up,
Manueri would have retired to bed for a week or two, genuinely
believing himself unable to work.

Opposite the dispensary and a bit further along the road was the
petrol pump. This was of immense value to us since the Land-
Rover required constant refuelling and the nearest commercial
pump was seventeen miles away, while here at the mill we were a
mere seven miles from home. Robin Knight, the manager of the
mill, had kindly given us permission to use the mill's facilities
and so there I was, in the heart of Africa, with no more to do than
sign my name on the bill for a full tank, and pay later. The existence of the mill had, of course, been a factor in deciding us to
work in the Budongo Forest in the first place. But we could not
help feeling favoured in comparison with those early explorers of
a hundred or even fifty years ago, trudging exhausted through the
elephant grass, unable to conceive of life as we could now
enjoy it.

And we were not isolated like those early pioneers: the mill
had a telephone link with Masindi and operated a daily mail
service to and from Masindi Post Office. Letters from home
arrived at the mill within a week and then it was simply a matter
of time until we came up and collected them. We felt we were in
contact with the outside world, and it was a comforting thought.
The mill's nerve centre, from which these facilities operated, was
a single raised wooden building with a verandah and a Union
Jack (replaced in October by the Uganda flag with its crested
crane) hanging from a tall flagpole outside. There were four
rooms: on the left Robin Knight's office, then mill engineer
David Kershaw's, then assistant manager George Barrow's, and
lastly the general office in which numerous African and Asian
clerks sat at desks. It was a pleasant building with a busy atmo-

sphere and could have been the headquarters of any big commercial undertaking anywhere, except that now and again the
crash of a lorry emerging from the forest with a felled giant, and
the steady beating of the overhead sun, reminded one of where
one was.

The mill itself, with its giant ten-inch bandsaws perpetually
screaming, was a huge building to the left from the office steps,
open at both ends. The scene inside was hugely impressive. A
hundred Africans, of the four hundred employed by the mill,
moved about their tasks, some high up in the rafters, bringing
the enormous trees into alignment with the blades, moving them
relentlessly forwards, backwards, an inch to the left, then forwards again until the first clean slice had been removed from the
trunk, part of the six hundred tons of sawn timber produced each
month. The din was immense, with two or three saws working
at once and Africans shouting to each other, piling up cut planks
and preparing them for the smaller circular saws at the far end
of the building where the edges would be trimmed in order to
remove the bark and bring the planks to standard widths. The
useless timber was thrown out on to huge heaps of 'kuni' (firewood), which was then collected by the boilermen for the mill's
own boilers, and by other firms and individuals – including ourselves – for household uses. A background symphony to all this
clatter was the roar of the diesel generators in the adjoining
building. Driven by steam from huge boilers, they greedily
consumed vast quantities of wood fuel, producing electricity for
the whole mill, including the hundred horse-power motors
which drove the saws. And on top of all this, in the same building,
was Bob Angus's vehicle repair department, with trucks being
dismantled and engines being tuned, the sharp heavy clatter of
steel on steel and a hundred shouted orders and questions and
jokes flying through the air.

One could do little but stand and stare. These African men
knew the part they played, and worked with precision. They
clearly enjoyed the power of working with heavy equipment, the
heaviest of its kind in all Uganda. They were the lucky few,
the five per cent with jobs, in this under-employed kingdom of
Bunyoro: a motley bunch of tough migrant labourers. Their
home lives had been disrupted and the control of tradition over

their behaviour was weak: they could be called the first victims in this area of industrialisation. They were toughened from hard work and living among strangers in a strange country. But they had money and freedom to do what they liked with it, the prestige of the wage earner over his family and friends who work the earth and are tied to one spot for ever.

One thing this money brought them was meat. Every Saturday a little group of cattle, lean and heavy-horned, could be seen making its way up the track towards the mill under the guardianship of a couple of equally skinny herdsmen. Believe it or not, this party was in the process of finishing a hundred and fifty mile trek on foot from the north. Poor cattle! It was well for them they did not know that their long and tiring journey led to the slaughterhouse: perhaps they imagined some sweet grassy plain on the banks of a crystal river in which they would slake their thirst. Arrived at the mill they were instantly despatched and then cut up with a hatchet by the mill's 'butcher'. As work ended at noon on Saturday and word got about that the meat had arrived, a huge queue formed outside the butcher's 'shop', a wire mesh enclosure, and each man (ourselves included) took away his share of the spoils, until everything was gone and even the huge heaps of guts had disappeared. This meat was known locally as 'Budongo beef'; it had to be well cooked owing to the numerous inhabitants of those West Nile cattle; and since they had lived a lifetime at bare subsistence level, and were hardier than cattle in more favourable climes anyway, the resulting beef was extraordinarily tough – outmatched only, in my experience, by elephant meat. Sinews seemed to be the rule rather than the exception and at times we might as well have been eating our shoes. Frequently we were forced to abandon supper on account of jaw-ache. What nutritive value there was in that meat I cannot imagine, but it was amazing how avidly everyone bought it and ate it, how we Europeans and the Indians and the Africans all shared a desperate desire for meat. Man, I was left in little doubt, is a natural carnivore.

Pay-day came on the first Saturday of the month, and that was when the revels really began. For few of these Africans saved their money; they feared thieves, and had, for the most part, no long-term projects which required savings. Most men spent their

wages quickly on clothes, food and drink, the proportion allocated to each varying from man to man. On pay-day Saturday
mornings a constant stream of women could be seen making
their way up the road toward the mill; some had children with
them, all had heavy loads on their heads. They were carrying
their produce as far as ten miles to sell it at the mill's Saturday
market: sweet potatoes, maize, tomatoes, avocados, passion fruit,
guavas, melons and bananas. Men could also be seen now, with
large gourds strapped to the panniers of their bicycles – each
gourd containing over a gallon of thick grey native beer. Everyone was happy in an abandoned way; after a month of frustrations
in which there was never enough money for anything, the end of
the month had come and money was a-plenty.

Down at the main road the impetus of the infection is felt too,
and here towards the middle of the afternoon a drum begins to
beat a steady boom-boom which will go on into the night. Small
groups of men and women stand in the sun talking, they wear
smiles. Girls begin to appear, neatly dressed and with their hair
done carefully. Young men, too, walk about confidently in the
best clothes they can muster. They go back into the square yard
where the drum is beating out its message and join the others
dancing on the bare earth floor. It is not a dance with steps but a
Congo dance, they shift their feet a little but rapidly, and let their
bodies twist and lean, losing the rhythm and gaining it again,
breaking off for a draught of 'pombe' beer from the big central
bowl or drinking it from a friend's gourd while dancing. Women
turn their backs and wiggle their bottoms provocatively, the
men respond with shouts and jumps, the drum is joined by a
guitar and some adapted bicycle pumps. The afternoon light is
failing, some are already leaving with their friends to stroll homewards through the tropical dusk; the rest drink and talk and
dance on.

But down in the forest behind the huts, there is something
sinister going on. Half a mile into the trees, in a spot known only
to a hard-core few, under a giant fig tree, 'warigi' is being consumed in earnest. 'Warigi', double distilled from beer, is colour-
less, aphrodisiac and enormously intoxicating. 'Warigi' is illegal,
and a man will go to prison for up to three years if he is found
making it. Distilled in swamps and other inaccessible places with

L

the use of copper tubing, 'warigi' sells at three shillings a bottle among men who know they can trust each other: men who are addicted. Manueri, I regret to say, was one such. Not that he ever distilled the stuff or even knew where this took place, nor even that he *had* to drink it every now and again. But if he had the money, he spent it on 'warigi', rather than clothes or meat, which I never knew him buy. He could drink two bottles and be all right next day, three bottles and he had to stay in bed. Normal men lose all self-control after a single bottle.

The trouble with 'warigi', we were told, and the reason it is illegal, is that not only is it dangerously strong spirit, but owing to the poisons in it it too often has the long term effect of making men insane or actually killing them. If it were properly distilled this would not occur, and thus there is an argument for the whole 'warigi' business being brought into the open. But if this did occur the amount of drunkenness and alcoholism might increase enormously. Africans told me it was unfair that Europeans should be allowed to buy whisky (prohibitively expensive for themselves) while they were not allowed to buy 'warigi', and I could not answer them that whisky has no ill-effects on the drinker for that is patently untrue. Nor could I say that whisky is more expensive than warigi and that Europeans drink less as a result, for in comparison with his earning power a bottle of whisky costs a European no more than a bottle of 'warigi' costs an African, and there is no doubt that some white men drink far more than is good for them. The Africans certainly had a point. But at the same time, it was clear that 'warigi' would have to be kept fairly scarce. Since Independence, the Uganda government has made a major change in the 'warigi' laws. A new central distillery has been built near Kampala, to produce a predetermined quantity of 'legal warigi', for distribution and sale under licence all over the country. All private production of 'warigi' will remain illegal. Whether this legal 'warigi' will reach those who need it, and whether the new distillery will eliminate the need for private stills, or coexist with them, remains to be seen. Certainly it will not be possible to reduce the total 'warigi' consumption. And I would not, myself, want to take away this fiendish pleasure from such poor people whose lives have little enough excitement; not all of them go raving mad. Manueri may have been beastly when he was drunk, but sober he had a depth of personality which is rare in more inhibited folk: despite, or perhaps because of, his monthly transgressions of the liquor laws, he had a wisdom of which I would be proud.

*

When Okenyi goes out to hunt for elephant, he leaves before dawn. Waking instinctively half an hour before the black sky turns red and the hyraxes stop their calling, he pulls on his khaki sweater with GAME written on it in big red letters at the front, puts on his shorts, winds khaki puttees around his legs starting under the foot and ending below the knee, laces his heavy boots, then feels for his rifle. He checks his ammunition, buttons his bush jacket, and is gone. If you come looking for Okenyi at dawn, his hut is already empty.

This is when he goes out alone, to hunt through the day and return at nightfall. It is different when he stays out longer, for then he goes accompanied by his fellow game guard, Okello, and each of them has a porter to carry food and blanket. In that way they can stay out for days. But I think Okenyi prefers to hunt alone; his skill outmatches his friend's, he sees more, and moves more silently.

Marco Okenyi is an Acholi, a hunter by training and a Game Guard by profession. He is tall, some six feet or more, and slim. His eyes are sharp and intelligent and his wit is instantaneous. The local Africans gather round him: he is a natural leader. They respect him because he is a killer of many elephants; they keep friends with him because he gives them meat; they laugh with him because he is companionable; they get drunk with him because he has money for beer. Okenyi also has money for wives, and at present he has four. The first was a church wedding, for Marco is a Catholic. The rest were common law weddings, without fuss and bother – a payment to the girl's father, with money-back guarantee if she was unsatisfactory. Marco has between ten and twenty children – it is impossible to count them all. He probably knows how many there are, but I forgot to ask him.

Now, as he walks along the track a faint greyness is already appearing in the sky through the leaves, but below in the forest the blackness of night persists. A late hyrax roars in a tree above him, its raucous growl rising with each burst to a frenzied pitch, as if survival depended on it. A mile inside the forest dawn is reaching the forest floor as Okenyi watches a leopard, a leopard he knows well and which knows him and knows it is safe from the gun. Twitching its tail, the leopard watches the man pass by from its resting place in the low branch of a tree, and watches him disappear round a far bend before resting its head on its paws again. Next, Okenyi comes upon a flock of kangas (guinea fowl) feeding on the track ahead of him, thirty of them at least, each one a tasty, filling supper of delicious tender white meat. But what can he do? With his big ·404 he would distintegrate a bird completely. On top of which his rounds are accountable to the Game Department. And finally he doesn't want to make a noise, for two reasons: firstly he doesn't want to scare off any elephants that may be around, and secondly he is still close to camp – if he shot they would hear it and start speculating. All this he wants to avoid. But how ridiculously unaware of him the kangas are! He walks right up to them in the dim misty morning, wishing he had a bow and arrow – anything but this huge elephant-stopper in his hand. They scatter finally to right and left and some flap up into the branches, the green-blue gloss of their spotted feathers glinting in the first rays of sunlight near the tops of the trees.

Okenyi walks on, his tread as regular as a clock, his senses and his mind open, absorbing every detail of the scene around him. An elephant-shrew trots on to the track ahead of him and he stops to watch. 'Sasa tembo' they call it in Swahili, with a grin: 'like an elephant' – the name is a joke; if you ask people what it is called they always say 'sasa tembo' and grin. The shrew sniffs the air; Okenyi is a tree stump. It scratches its cheek with a hind foot. It has big, mobile ears. It is not at first sight like a shrew: far too big, eight inches long with a few more inches of tail, but its nose is elongated, shrew-fashion, into a proboscis, and hence the name. It trots on, into the forest.

It is light now and Okenyi begins a cigarette. He has crossed two bridges and he is about two miles into the forest as the hornbill flies. He leaves the main track and follows a Forest Department boundary marking the borderline between two 'compartments' of forest which have been tended since felling thirty years ago, to ensure a good crop of timber trees. Okenyi's job is to see that elephants are kept out of these compartments, for elephants are the greatest menace to silviculture here, with their passion for the delicate taste of the mahogany sapling. He is now walking between two compartments on a boundary that runs as straight as an arrow from east to west, as far as the forest edge. Every now and then a mass of undergrowth around a fallen tree has to be negotiated, but he knows all of these spots and the tracks around them: little notches on the trees guide him. Old buffalo prints, and the prints of pigs and antelopes do not interest him beyond a brief examination: these too he knows individually, even the time when they first appeared. Monkeys leap away as he passes, or sit with jerky head movements spluttering and chirruping as they watch him.

Finally he reaches the spot where, yesterday, Forest Department workmen heard an elephant browsing, waiting just long enough to make sure it was not a buffalo before they fled. Okenyi knows the exact spot for it was described to him at length the evening before; tree by tree in their minds, Okenyi and the Forest men came to this very spot; there could be no mistake between men who knew the forest so well. Okenyi now knows that he has to go three hundred paces to the north in order to reach the spot where the elephant was heard, and he also knows that it will not be there now. So first he walks on up the track to see if it has crossed. It has not. Returning to the spot he enters the forest. Counting his steps he heads north, following the track of the Forest Department men. He reaches the place where they were working: some of the trees are newly ringed. A knife has been dropped in the hurry to leave. He thinks how useful it might be, shoulders his rifle by the strap, then decides against the knife and walks on carefully. He can already smell the dung. He reaches it.

Now Okenyi has to think hard. He puts down his gun and stands by the dung and looks at it. Standing on every side of the dung he looks up, slowly, noticing the pattern of broken branches and crushed leaves. The elephant's track is clear and he walks up it, first one way and then the other. A branch lies fallen across the track; on one side it is grazed and the white wood shows through. He squats to examine the graze. The skin of the branch has been pulled upwards. It is all he needs to know. This damage can only be the result of a foot being lifted over the branch and so he knows which way tembo, the elephant, was going. Shoulder-ing his weapon, Okenyi starts to follow the track. He is in no hurry, nor is he unduly careful in his movements: the dung is a day old. Judging from the size of the prints the beast is medium large, but something distresses Okenyi: he finds that while some of the prints are deep and regular (the depth being due not only to the weight of the animal but to the fact that it places its hind foot in the depression made by the forefoot) each alternate print is skewed strangely to one side, and a groove in front of the print shows that one foot is not picked up cleanly but leaves the ground with a dragging movement. Okenyi knows he is following an elephant with a limp, and that this may make it bad-tempered and sly. There is nothing in the whole forest as dangerous as a wounded elephant, except perhaps a wounded buffalo. These great beasts get so enraged at their unending torture – a torture which prevents them from sleeping, from following their kind, and which cannot be alleviated by resting because of the terrible pangs of hunger – that they turn evil, and with a mixture of cunning and madness prefer to face their enemy rather than flee, and as often as not kill him.

Okenyi continues to follow his injured quarry through the trees. He finds little dung and notices that the animal's footsteps are rather far apart. Perhaps the elephant had heard the work-men and was moving out of the area. He passes a tree under which lie large numbers of rotting fruits smelling of decay: this is an elephant delicacy, some say the fermenting fruits have an intoxicating effect. This elephant has not stopped; it was in a hurry.

Okenyi tracks his quarry to the edge of the forest and into the tall grassland beyond. He walks between the ten foot grass walls until his wiry legs are tired and his stomach contracts, he thinks of the enormous distance he must return for food. Resting in a forest outlier he debates whether to turn back. A big dark squirrel runs along a branch, and two smaller ones with stripes move around jerkily above, frisking their tails. These squirrels are often found near water: they live over swamps and rarely leave the trees. Looking carefully he sees the glint of water in a shaft of sunlight.

He goes over to the pool and drinks. As he drinks he smells the smell of elephant across the water. It is like the majestic theme of a symphony one knows well, a theme from the last movement: all that remains is the finale, and one wonders how well it will be performed.

Okenyi picks up his gun and presses his finger to release the safety catch. He has the smell in his dilated nostrils, his body is half bent, his eyes peering through the trees, his head is held forward. He takes a step, pauses, steps again, moving his head this way and that to see between the trees. The smell is strong, it fills the little patch of forest. Every shape is examined with knowledgeable eyes. Especially he looks for the rounded shapes of the elephant, or for a twitch of ears.

With a crash of trees being flung apart the beast moves to his right. He hadn't expected it there. Is it charging or fleeing? He raises his gun. All is quiet. Then he sees it between the trees, at least he sees a shape and knows it is the elephant, though he does not see enough yet. Gently he moves his head and body to get a better view, and finds that by crouching he can see an eye through the leaves. But before he can aim it charges him. At ten yards he aims. It is a young bull in the prime of life; he thinks: impetuous, it should have fled. A chilling shriek pierces the air as the rifle fires. It is a brain shot: death is instantaneous. There is a discordant groan and the elephant staggers, rolling on one side with stiff legs shivering in death. Leaves flutter down, shaken by his fall; insects resume their humming, all around animals resume their lives after the shocked silence when the giant shrieked and fell. Okenyi is tired and content, he looks at his kill and sees the gangrenous left hind foot where a wire snare, since shaken off, had become embedded in the flesh, a buffalo snare probably, never meant for elephant. The dead beast moves jerkily as its life escapes.

The day is humid and overcast as he leaves his kill to return home. From now until evening he carries his secret with him, for the shot could not be heard in camp six miles away. Tomorrow a hundred men will come to the elephant, to take its meat home for their wives and children. They will come on bicycles and on foot, even some women will undertake the journey. Each will carry home as much as he or she can; Okenyi's fame will ring around the villages. The game guards will take the tusks to be weighed and catalogued and sold, the ears for drying (they sell for twenty shillings dried and make excellent shoes and handbags when cured), the feet for paper-baskets, the tail-hairs as lucky charms. Tomorrow will see the elephant opened up and its giant guts displayed, men will wander into its belly cutting off huge slabs of meat. Some will carry it home raw, wrapped in sacking; others smoke it crudely over wood fires, turning it black all over, then pierce the sealed pieces with a pole which they will carry over the shoulder.

And the day after tomorrow nature will send in her squadrons to eat the leftovers. Ants will come, and flies. The flies will breed in thousands and their larvae will feed. Quickly the guts and the meat around the bones and the trunk and the eyes will disappear. Even the skin will be consumed, though it is horny and thick. Rain will wash the blood into the ground. Before a week is over, the huge bones will be displayed, lying in the centre of a small denuded glade, made by the men who first came to take meat and who cut the nearby saplings to make fires and carrying stakes.

Then, months after, we shall come to the spot in our wanderings and see the strewn bones, mouldering now under a fine green mossy cover. We shall stop and look at the wreck and I shall ask Manueri to chip me out a tooth from the jaw, to take home as a souvenir.

*

One day in April I was up at the mill collecting mail, the day was humid and people were moving about slowly, with a minimum of effort, creeping between the wooden huts as if ashamed of something. Even the giant saws sounded dull and subdued as they ate their way through slice after slice of giant mahogany. I read a letter from England sitting on the office steps, and looked over my latest Kodachrome film to see if there were any good shots of chimpanzees in it. I had just got up to go over to the Land-Rover when the heavy peace of the afternoon was interrupted by a party of men returning from the logging point some miles up the track which ran due north. They were in a lorry, and as it passed me they were pointing and shouting something to me, and I thought it contained the word 'soko-mutu'. I smiled and waved back, embarrassed by this sudden unexpected out-burst from twenty or thirty excited men, all directed at me. When the lorry stopped two or three of the men came back to me, and I gathered from their gestures and bits of what they said that a chimpanzee had been caught. It was up the road "milei mbili" (two miles) or something like that. Dropping all other plans, I jumped into the Land-Rover and headed up along the north track.

How had they caught it? In a snare? Was it dead, or had they made a cage? My main problem was to find the spot. Some men pointed further up the road, but they probably hadn't understood my question, and I had learned to distrust people who simply pointed up the road. I took a number of dead-end forks and turned back. Then an empty timber lorry came along heading for the logging point. I drove into the edge of the forest to let him pass, then followed his bouncing articulated chassis with its chains and springs banging and crashing along through the dust until sud-denly, ahead of us, was a big group of Africans, red bulldozers, freshly felled and trimmed trees awaiting collection, and a wide open space beyond: the logging area.

The men were sitting in a circle, on logs or on the ground, laughing. In the middle of the circle, tied to a stake, with her arms stretched up above her head and her legs stretched down, lay an old female chimpanzee, a dear old lady, such as many I had seen going about their unobtrusive business in the forest. As I joined the circle of onlookers they continued to joke, while the poor creature alternately shrieked with fear or hooted to her fled com-panions, turning her head to left and right as she lay on her back, and looking at me piteously as I examined her bonds. She was firmly tied up, by the wrists and ankles, as a wild pig or duiker is tied, so that it can be carried. How far, I wondered, had they brought her, how much had she endured?

I was no missionary; I knew that in Uganda the African's attitude to wild animals in general was catch and kill and eat. The very same word, 'nyama', is Swahili for both 'animal' (alive) and 'meat' (dead or cooked). I had learnt not to expect sympathy and soft feelings for animals in Africa. Yet I had until now believed that the chimpanzee was regarded in a different way from

other creatures, that it was a 'half-man', whom one respected and
left alone and, in particular, never ate. Indeed, generally this was
so.

I looked around at the logging men. They were a mixed crowd,
from the Congo and Ruanda and all parts of Uganda. In the
eastern Congo, I had been told, the people still ate chimpanzees,
as they had done in Livingstone's day, ninety years ago.

The men were watching me now, waiting to see my reaction
to the situation. Conscious of the imperfections of my Swahili, I
started battle. "Where did you catch this chimpanzee?" I asked,
to all and sundry. There was no reply, nobody wanted to talk.
I think they sensed my fury. I picked on one man. "Over there?"
I asked, "or over there?" Suddenly a boy broke ranks with a flood
of words, pointing to his leg, and another boy joined him. I
gathered that they had been working when the chimp attacked the
boy and wanted to kill him. The boy had fought and cried out
whereupon four men had between them pinned the creature
down. I looked at his leg – it was scratched slightly – little white
scratch marks covered it, such as Manueri got from walking
through the rattan. "Where is the blood?" I asked, "if the
chimpanzee attacked you, where are the wounds?"

A man threw a hard piece of fruit to the chimpanzee, hitting it
on the head. I gave up a reasoned approach, and shouted at them
all. "Watcha!" – "Leave it! This is bad. It is bad to catch a chimpanzee, bad to tie it up, this is a good animal. This is not food, it
is not a duiker. And it is not a lion to be afraid of. I am angry
that you have caught it; now we will let it go!"

I summoned two men to take the pole, told the rest to wait
behind and walked into the forest. This was mainly in order that
they would not be able to follow her, and also to avoid the risk
of her attacking, in case she really was dangerous. She never
ceased her howling and screaming. We walked a short distance
in, then set her down. I undid her legs – she did not kick wildly
as I had expected her to, but fell silent. Gently and without showing fear, I began to unleash her arms. I was expecting at any
moment that she would spring up and leap away from us, disappearing forever into the trees. Instead she lay there, placidly
watching me as I undid her wrists, a look of what seemed great
sadness in her eyes. I ordered the men to stand back and pulled

the liana free as gently as I could. Her arms fell out sideways, she moved them a little, she tried to turn on her side, her legs moved a little, she looked at me in despair. She was unable to move away.

During the next half hour I felt her all over to see how she was hurt, and discovered an injury to her spine, half way along the back. It was visible under the skin – the vertebrae suddenly changed direction. She could still move her legs a little, but would never walk again.

As she lay on the ground in front of me with pleading eyes, I knew the most merciful thing to do would be to kill her. With a rifle shot, death would be instantaneous, but my gun was sixteen miles away. Or I could cut her throat with a panga. Looking at her, she seemed so intensely human that I could not bear the thought: it would be pure murder. I told the men to stay here and wait for my return; they were to watch the chimpanzee and see if her condition improved; I would be back in one hour with the gun. I slipped them a shilling each and left, satisfied I had made the right choice.

In fact, I had been thoroughly foolish. But that is jumping ahead too far. When I left, passing through the lines of workmen whose fun I had spoiled, I felt their eyes burning through my neck. They probably thought I was stupid and pathetic, letting a prize like that go free. I hoped they would not notice that the two men who went in with me did not come out. And, in all probability they would not have noticed; but then knocking-off time arrived.

So, as I was driving back as fast as I could go for my gun, bouncing and slithering down the sawmill track, a rota was being called back at the logging area as the day's work ended. And before I had even reached home a search was on for the missing men and they were found and so was the chimpanzee. That, at any rate is my theory: I never discovered the truth. When I returned not a soul was around, there was nothing in the spot where the old mother chimp had been except the pole she was strung to and a few broken lianas. There were no chimpanzee footprints away from the spot, there was also no blood. Birds sang in the trees, among them a yellow-bill which cackled at me. A light wind moved the treetops and the first wisps of cloud were

forming overhead. Insects droned in the strong vertical shafts of
sunlight: nowhere was there any evidence of the little drama
which had unfolded here. The end must have been sinister and
tragic; I did not think about it. Climbing back into the Land-
Rover, with a final curse at my stupidity, I realized I was totally
exhausted, and started the bumpy drive home.

CHAPTER EIGHT

Tracking and Finding

It is dawn; let us set off on foot and look for chimpanzees. We shall follow some forest tracks. First, we go down to the main road and turn left. Two hundred yards along on the right a vehicle track goes off through fifty yards of grassland dotted about with cork trees and plunges into the forest. This is a Forest Department road, the one we took on our first day; we have christened it Track A. It is cut twice a year, and in addition fallen trees are cleared as they occur in order to keep the road open at all times. We use this road more than any other; I know every bump and rut along it, when to drive on the left and when on the right, where to park, where to turn, how to cross the plank bridge at the bottom of the first slope. Also we have walked down it in-numerable times. There are snares along it, set by Forest Department workmen, and we remove these as we find them. Animal tracks criss-cross it every few yards along – old ones mainly, which we already know. A civet has its lavatory in the middle of the road – a big pile of fruit stones and black faecal matter, which grows a little from time to time. To the right a quarter of a mile down is our own track to the fig tree where we watched chimps every day for a week in April, a little farther is the spot where we once lay to watch them crossing the road. An elephant shrew which lives here – the one Okenyi saw – crosses ahead of us. Down at the bridge we look at the gurgling Bubwe on its way to Lake Albert with some of the forest's surplus rainfall. Here is where I shot the black-lipped cobra. Now we reach Track R.P.5 leading off at right angles to the right, a forest trace marking the boundary between two plots, and heading due south. Ahead is a stretch of a hundred yards on which we often see a male blue duiker browsing along the verge of the road, but he is not here today. At the brow of the hill a party of redtail monkeys jumps around in the trees, squeaking at us and looking incensed, with white noses and rusty coloured tails darting about in among the greenery. We do not stop for they would only panic and run off. Distantly a blue monkey makes his alarm call "Kyoh!" and a colobus takes it up with its gargling, oft repeated belch.

We walk downhill now and there is, as always, a puddle at the bottom. We have never seen any living thing in this dip, although the forest is perfectly ordinary. That is an odd thing, however, and recurrently true – that along any given road or journey, some spots are always full of wild life and others are completely empty. At the top of the slope we curve right and are joined by what we call Track B, cutting in at an angle from our right-hand side. To the left a forest track, heavily overgrown, goes due north. Ahead of us now is Little Kasenene hill, which we see from our home, but it cannot be seen from the forest floor and our road goes past it, leaving it unseen on the right-hand side. As we pass the hill a large troop of baboons fills the road ahead, looking at us, scampering about, wiping their snouts, stamping their feet, and barking: "wo-hrrr, wo-hrr, wo, wo." There are mothers with infants clinging under them, others with infants on their backs, young skinny ones, medium sized ones, and big bully males with huge ruffs making their heads look round from the front and their eyes small like pigs'. They are a uniformly olive colour. As we draw nearer they hop and run, one by one, into the forest.

Past Little Kasenene the road begins a long wind around towards the left (north). We pass the place of the dead trees where we gather 'kuni' (firewood), the overgrown track leading off to the right which used to lead to the mill and was used for logging, but is now almost invisible in places and used mainly by buffaloes, whose tracks have made ruts in the grass. Further along on the right is our marker to the tree we discovered one day, a tall beautiful tree with fruits the size of tennis balls and peach-coloured, full of sticky orange flesh from which the white latex poured copiously; Manueri bit into the fruits greedily after examining them, and said they were "mzuri sana, sasa pombe!" (very good, like beer!) and vowed to return and collect more as they fell. We later discovered this species to be *Mammea africana*, a very rare tree found, in Uganda, only in the Budongo Forest. Past this marker the road dips, rises, and turns to the point where it doubles back on itself, from north west to north east. At this point a forest trace we call R.P.2 heads off in a line towards the west, continuing past the Forest Department store, where diesel and spraying equipment used in the poisoning of trees are kept in a round tin hut, right up to the edge of the forest. Following Track A (but we shall go no farther) we could fork left farther ahead along a road which leads out of the forest amid a flourish of flame trees, into the elephant grass and to the river Sonso beyond, wide here and uncrossable; or we could take the right fork which stays inside the forest and meanders gently downwards, with elephant trails to left and right, to the sad wreck of the Sonso river bridge, brought down some months ago by a swollen river and now, with its structure weakened and some of its planks missing, in urgent need of repair. The broken bridge is in a delightful glade, the river gurgles here on its way through, and for some reason grass grows beneath the Ironwood trees. Crossing the bridge by foot is still possible, but the glade is so enchanting, and the road ahead so overgrown, that we have never gone much farther than this point.

No chimpanzees call; the morning is lost. Feeling hungry, we settle down with our backs to trees and Frankie pulls the sand-wiches out of our leather bag. One sandwich each, Budongo beef as ever. Manueri politely takes his with an "Asante sana mama" – "Thank you very much mother." We all begin chewing, the meat defends itself remorselessly. Little crumbs of bread fall on to the leaves and we watch as, almost immediately, ants col-lect them and take them off, two or three working together on the larger ones, to their home in some nearby crevice or perhaps up in a tree.

Manueri makes one of his cigarettes and lights up, the dense grey smoke turns blue as it coils upwards in shafts of sunlight between the trees. We lean back, resting, Suddenly Manueri says "Ndege" – "a bird". Distantly, we detect the faintest droning far up in the sky; coming a little closer, it is definitely an aero-plane, the first we have heard for months. We listen carefully as it comes a very little closer and then passes out of earshot, bound on its distant purpose. We find a smile on our lips, Frankie and I, for it reminds us of a whole world whose existence we have forgotten, a frantic civilization hurrying, hurrying.

"Sisi nakuja hapa kwa ndege sasa hi," I venture to Manueri: "We came out here on a plane like that one."

"Oh!" – his whole expression invites me to go on.

"A plane is not small, it is big, and heavy!"

"Oh! As big as an elephant!"

"Bigger!"

"Oh! Completely big!"

"Yes. And fifty people can go in it!"

"Fifty?" he is incredulous. "No" – he rejects the idea.

"Yes, fifty and more! And we came here above the clouds!"

"Phew" – his long-drawn whistle of astonishment. "The plane goes above the clouds? It must be very hot."

"No, it is very cold outside the plane, but good inside. If you look out of the plane you can see the forests, and the plains and the mountains – everything!"

"Good." He imagines himself up there, looking down, then fear strikes him. "Mimi hapana penda ndege" – "I don't like planes."

"Why not?"

"That's very far up. Bad. If there is a breakdown, boom!" gesturing with a downwards sweep of his hand.

"Yes," we agree. "That is bad. But if you travel many days on foot you may eat bad food and die; in the plane the food is very good and the journey is very quick. How long do you think it takes to go to Ingereza (England)?"

"Wiki tatu," he guesses – "three weeks."

"No. From Entebbe to London it takes eleven hours."

"Ow! The plane goes pessi-pessi – very quickly! Eleven hours, and England is beyond West Nile!"

"Beyond West Nile," we point out, "is the Sudan. The Sudan is bigger than all of Uganda. Beyond the Sudan is Egypt. Egypt is bigger than all of Uganda. Beyond Egypt is a big sea with much water, which is bigger than Uganda. Beyond that sea is Europe, Europe is bigger than all of Uganda. At the other side of Europe is England."

We are all speechless for a while at the thought of it.

"It needs many shillings to go to London," he says.

"Yes. Many shillings. How many do you think?"

"People say it needs two thousand shillings."

"Yes. That is right," we are surprised he knows. He shakes his head and says "A-a". We get up and start walking, slowly, for the mention of that vast sum had made the conversation sad. Not that he is envious; he has never even had the desire to go to Kampala. But the social inequality between us has been exposed and we are aware of it, each with an equal regret.

We now return down Track A to the junction with Track B and follow that road. It leads off through grassland, circuiting the hill, and here red-legged partridges, or francolins, feed on the path. They are alert because of the barks of baboons watching us from arboreal posts up the hillside. After half a mile we enter the forest through its surrounding jacket of *Maesopsis* trees. It quickly ages and becomes higher, more diverse and more grown about with lianas and the other trappings of maturity until we are on a gentle slope down to the Lwenti River. This slope is favoured by guinea fowl and I have often shot them here, also I have twice watched a ram bushbuck which frequents these parts, and admired the beauty of his spots and stripes and his foot-long horns. The river itself is bridged over for vehicles to pass, but the surrounding land and indeed the whole valley is marshy, marked on the map of forest types as Swamp Forest. This is the result of the shape of the valley which, perhaps because it is a new water-course, is not a deep cut into the soil but a mere declivity on either side, and the river meanders down the middle in a hundred little rivulets interspersed with marshland and the trees and creepers that grow on it: rattan, *Pseudospondias*, the liane which if you cut a piece of it off, pours forth water that you can drink, and others. So, when crossing the Lwenti bridge by vehicle, I have learnt to take it at a good speed or risk getting stuck in the mud on the gently rising far slope; but today on foot this is a pleasant bridge to linger by, and look along the marshy valley with its unusual trees and squirrels and insects and, above all, frogs. Round the next bend we reach the spot where a particular tree used to stand. One day, as we were walking through the forest, we heard a tree fall and Manueri said it was this very tree and it was. He had seen its gigantic frailty weeks before. When it fell, after a rainstorm, it came down like a house of cards, straight downwards not sideways, in little pieces, rotten through and through.

Farther along is the place where we ourselves were struck by a falling tree as we drove down the road. We were bumping along

M

when all of a sudden, for no reason that I could see, I lost all
control and the Land-Rover went straight round into the forest
on the left-hand side of the track. I thought the steering must
have gone. We got out a bit bruised but uninjured and, looking
backwards, saw that the whole of the road behind us was blocked
by the topmost branches of a big tree which must, at the instant
of our passing, have been falling towards the road from its
position a hundred feet inside the forest. A branch had caught the
Land-Rover slap across the roof, tearing the canvas to shreds
and wrenching the metal roof frame off, but there was no other
damage. Had the tree fallen a fraction of a second sooner, the
branch would have landed on our heads. We looked at the fallen
tree – it was one which had been poisoned by the Forest Department, until then our biggest benefactors in Uganda. With a few
muttered curses we backed out on to the track and continued on
up to the mill for roof repairs.

Track B was quite a track for falling wood. A little farther
along from the place where we were struck we found, one day, a
huge limb of an otherwise healthy mahogany tree lying across the
road. The branch itself was almost as thick as a man's height, for I
afterwards used it as a blind when out after kanga, and shot one
at a hundred yards with the gun resting on it. Why had it
dropped? Perhaps a tornado had struck it, and I mean that
seriously, for we had a tornado one night at the bottom of our
hill and it brought down a row of trees like a giant scythe. Past
this great leafy chunk of fallen mahogany which left a great red-
brown wound a hundred feet up on the side of its parent, the
track runs straight for several hundred yards and there are
usually monkeys, redtails, or colobus, along this stretch. At the
bottom is a giant 'Mukunyu' fig tree on the right but it is not in
season now. Then the track turns right and right again and we
are out on the road to the sawmill, standing on murram, with
every now and then a man on foot or on a bicycle going by.

Still no chimp calls. It is a bad day. Tired as we are, we must
try somewhere else. We go down to the dusty, red main road,
turn right, and walk along it a full mile towards Busingiro until
we reach a spot where, on the right, is a white mile-stone saying
'27' on the near side and '17' on the far side – twenty-seven miles
to Masindi, seventeen to Butiaba the other way. Behind this stone

the bank of the road rises – three feet or so of exposed red soil; it is covered in grass on top, and three feet or so behind this bank is the edge of the forest. Looking carefully, a hole can be seen at this point and, taking care not to slip as the bank slopes steeply downwards through the hole, we enter the forest. Ahead of us is a forest trace running due east, it marks the boundary between two forest department plots, and is cleared once a year. We call it the Mile 27 East track. We walk along it between *Maesopsis* trees at first, on a gentle downhill slope, conscious of the coolness of the air under the trees. A short way along is a fallen tree trunk which can be crossed as follows: you step on the branch, which is firm and springy and about a foot off the ground; from this you step up on to the main trunk – careful, it is slippery and inclined to crumble – walk along it obliquely to the track for four paces and then jump off. Ahead we approach the First Valley. This is very steep and we leave the east track, going very slightly off to the left where our stakes are waiting for us. We take one each and begin the descent, picking our steps on the firmer parts of the ground, either using the stick to lean on or sticking it into the ground just ahead and stepping on the ground behind it so that the stick itself is holding the foot from slipping. We get to the bottom, where the Bubwe river trickles along between large and small stones, with shrubs growing in the mud and the footpads of a leopard between the shrubs, hoofprints of a red duiker too, and a yellow caterpillar with long black hair and red eyes sitting on a leaf. We cross the river over stepping stones. On the far side the fruits of a 'Mujgangoma' tree litter the forest floor, looking like huge acorns complete with cups, but they are sticky inside and have a stone; we turn left and follow the bank of the stream a few yards, crawl under a fallen tree which is worn smooth with the rubbing of our backs, and rejoin the east track for the ascent. Now we use our sticks to push on as we clamber slowly up the slippery slope, finding step-like footholds wherever we can. To our right is a fig tree visited by the chimpanzees when it is in fruit but at present it isn't. A little pale-blue flower, like a pansy, shows through the shrubs. At the top we stick our sticks into their accustomed place near a rotten tree stump, ready for the return. The ground now slopes gently upwards. A group of colobus monkeys flashes black and white, crashing from branch to branch with great leaps in the treetops ahead. We pass three Ironwood trees which throw their buttresses across our path like a barrier, and find a porcupine's quill under one of them. At the top of the gentle slope is a big flat stone. We start downwards on the undulation. So far Manueri today has not used the knife, an index of our ill-luck; we have not exerted ourselves, walking along at a steady pace, silently, in tune with the forest. For a fallen tree we leave the path, turning off after a smooth-barked tree, to the left, going in a wide semicircle marked by chips on the trees, stepping over a fallen branch two feet up and rejoining the east track at the slope towards the second valley. Again the steep descent but here, for some reason, we do not use sticks. To our left a giant mahogany lies across the entire valley, an enormous bridge, but we do not use it for a slip would mean a drop of thirty feet. This is a dry valley – not even after rain does a proper stream run along it – yet it must in the past have been a big carving stream like the Bubwe. A recently fallen tree lies along the line of our path on the far side of the valley: we use its small resilient branches to pull ourselves up, but it is a nuisance and we ought to make a detour at this point. Manueri stops and points: a bushbuck stands ahead of us on the track, he turns and leaps into the forest with a shattering bark, then two or three more, each more muffled than the last as he runs into the trees: "Wo!!! Wo!! Wo!" Birds do not cease their calling for his alarm, soft piping notes and cackles and the distant caw-cawing of hornbills go on unabated; the flashing scarlet of a butterfly catches our eye; we go on up the slope. Here a liana hangs in a vertical line, dropping one hundred and fifty feet from a branch and still not reaching the ground, its red, naked roots suspended in the air searching for soil, growing slowly downwards. There is no wind above, the leaves are still.

Chimpanzee calls ahead! There are some in the third valley. We go on at a slightly quickened pace, the path widens out a little here and begins to slope very gently downwards, Manueri uses the knife sometimes to slice through the *Marantochloa* shrubs with their juicy stems and broad leaves, they fall sideways like toppled pins, leaving us a clear path. The Third Valley is not steep, indeed there is no true valley, just a gentle slope to the bottom. Leaving the track to our left, we go more slowly now, picking our way between the trees, pausing every now and then to scan the tree-tops ahead. We reach the spot where there are some 'Muyati' trees (*Mildbraediodendron*) which we know to be fruiting, and stop to listen. We sit down to wait; we are too close to risk moving now. All is still, then a quarrel breaks out ahead, excited screaming and some gruff barks. We know just where they are, and we edge forward, step by step.

First we see an adult male sitting on a branch, chewing a strip of bark. He moves out of the way as another male comes along – did the latter snatch his bark? There are screams and a brief chase in the trees behind. An adolescent male with a pale face appears on a branch of the Muyati – he thumps the branch with his feet, holding on with his arms. The adult male scratches himself, then begins feeding on the big green Muyati fruits, peeling them first with his teeth, then chewing up the flesh inside (which looks like cucumber) and finally spitting out the rest of the peel in a chewed-up mass. He moves off looking for food, out of sight. We wait. Manueri settles down and lights a cigarette.

After a few minutes a mother walks into sight, her toto clinging beneath her belly. She sits down and feeds, the baby drops to the branch and gingerly walks along it, to a big elephant's-ear fern which it slaps with one hand. It has a pink face and a white 'tail tuft'. All is quiet but for the buzzing of insects and bird calls, and the occasional rustle of leaves, as a chimpanzee strips off a branch for food, and the thud-thud of over-ripe fruits as they fall to the ground.

We watch, and make notes, for an hour: we see five chimps; sometimes they call but never very loudly. One by one they drift away, out of sight, and then deep into the forest: we follow a little but without conviction – it is growing late and we shall not see them again – and so we consult, and decide to turn for home.

*

Working outwards from our base at Busingiro Hill, we had found that the most useful thing we could do was to concentrate all our efforts on an area of about sixteen square miles, within which we could, most days, hear a group somewhere or other. This we called our study area and although we frequently went beyond it to follow up particular groups or for other reasons, the bulk of our work was done within this chunk of trees. Every forest type was represented here, although there was not much Iron-wood Forest, but this type, we had established, was not very favourable chimpanzee habitat anyway. Our chunk was mainly Mixed Woodland, and *Maesopsis* forest, with its fair share of swamps, and we had both the solid mass of forest on the Budongo side, and the narrow strips of riverine forest in the Siba to work in. We found no area of natural forest which the chimpanzees shunned entirely, but we quickly established that certain areas were favourite chimp localities, and as time went by we saw how these favoured places changed every so often with the fruits and seasons.

We had gathered a lot of information in our first months about their feeding habits, daily routines, and social life, but our project title included a second heading, and one which began to interest us more and puzzle us more as time went by. That heading was 'social *organization*'. The idea that chimpanzees live in 'family groups' is widespread today, both in white societies and in Africa itself. Where this idea comes from it is impossible to say – is it perhaps that we humans tend to be anthropomorphic whenever we think of apes, and attribute our own kind of social life to them? Several authors have committed themselves to print on the point: David Livingstone, for instance, the much respected missionary, wrote of chimpanzees in his Last Journals: 'They live in communities of about ten, each having his own female. . . . If one tries to seize the female of another, he is caught on the ground, and all unite in boxing and biting the offender.' Is this not a case of Victorian family morality imposed on the chimp?

At all events, to judge from the writings of a good many naturalists who saw chimpanzees in the wild, no such family groups exist. Garner, for example, stated, "I have never been able to see a family of them together", and he reported that of several groups of chimpanzees that he had watched crossing an open space from one patch of forest to another, the groups numbered from two to ten individuals, and none consisted of a 'family'. Nissen's study of chimpanzees in West Africa produced no evidence of permanent groupings, family or otherwise.

Shortly before we set out for Uganda, Adriaan Kortlandt, a Dutch zoologist, had made a study of wild chimpanzees on a plantation site near Beni, in the East Congo, and had obtained no evidence of family groups. He had gone further, and said that there were no *permanent* groups of chimpanzees at all – that the animals come and go as they please; when they do join up, they form either 'nursery groups', consisting of a gathering of mothers and their infants, or 'sexual groups', consisting of adult males and females.

Besides this question of groups, there were two other problems which, we realized, were as yet totally uninvestigated, and naturally we determined to concentrate on them. One was the question of whether a particular number of chimpanzees could be thought of as a 'tribe', as opposed to other 'tribes' in the forest. And the second arose directly out of this – were there particular areas of forest which were more or less exclusively ranged over by particular sets of chimpanzees? Or were we faced with a large number of chimps – none of which knew or cared much about each other – which roamed the forest from one fruit area to another without any allegiance to, or special knowledge of, any particular tract of trees?

We guessed that we would need a vast body of information to be able to answer these complex questions. In the meantime we concentrated on the simpler issues. For a start, we compared the society of chimpanzees with that of baboons. Baboons live in 'troops', a troop being a number of primates which live together permanently. With chimpanzees, we came to realize, everything was different. In the fig season when we first began our observations, groups had been large and noisy, fifteen or more chimps on a tree. Then in the lean season, groups had been small and scattered and sometimes single individuals were encountered feeding alone. Then, in the Igeria season, once again we met with large noisy mixed feeding groups. There was never any indication that a group of chimpanzees was a constant unit.

For three weeks in June we had the opportunity to observe and examine the membership of chimpanzee groups at close quarters in good observation conditions. Over the study area the chief fruit in season was the damson-like Igeria, and we were finding it difficult observing in the swamps, because of recent heavy rainfall, and also because, at this season, chimps never seemed to stay long on one patch of Igeria trees, but were forever moving on after half an hour or so. We had to find somewhere better to continue our observations for the time being. Down the road towards Masindi was a large coffee estate called Kanyege and a neighbour, Don Baggeley, now told us that chimpanzees were calling there. Imagine our delight when one dismal misty dawn, we negotiated our Land-Rover, slithering and skidding along the wet muddy soil between the coffee bushes, to the far side of the estate where it bordered the forest, and Manueri spotted movements in the trees fringing the estate. "Soko-mutu!" he said. We stopped the vehicle and got out. Then, dodging from coffee bush to coffee bush, each time getting a cold shower of fresh rain down our necks, we approached the outline of trees. Arrived at the end of the bushes, and in direct view of the moving branches, we each selected a coffee bush as camouflage and sat down behind it to observe. We half expected disappointment – that the movements would turn out to be monkeys of some sort. But no, they were chimps, and they were feeding on Nyakatomas. We were in luck. They had not seen us. Every morning for the next three weeks chimps came to these trees, and we were there first thing every day, squatting damply behind our chosen coffee bushes, identifying, counting, and observing.

After a few hours, by mid-morning, the chimps in the trees at the edge of the estate left to visit other feeding areas, and at this point we would follow one group, though we found this particular stretch of the Siba forest very difficult to locate chimps in. It was a wavy finger of gallery forest fringing the Siba river, and the chimps always seemed to be calling on the opposite bank to us. The only way to cross the swollen river, which was fifteen to twenty feet wide, six feet deep, swirling and muddy, was to walk across by a fallen tree trunk straddling the stream. Manueri cut strong staffs from saplings for each of us and gingerly we edged our way across testing each foot-hold on the crumbling rotten logs.

But usually we expended enormous efforts in the Siba only to see the last chimpanzee leaving the trees, for these were a restless lot of chimps. One day they led us deep into the forest and out on to the grassland beyond, where we found the fresh green dung, still warm, of a herd of elephants which had been there only minutes previously. The Siba was 'kali' forest, as Manueri so often said.

But whereas inside the forest we gained little extra information, those hours from dawn at the Kanyege coffee estate yielded much raw material. Some chimps were there day after day, and always in a favourite spot in the clump of trees. There were two huge black-faced matrons, each with a three-year-old juvenile. The two juveniles played together while the mothers sat there solemnly reaching for fruit, plucking, chewing, spitting, and reaching again. Unlike human mothers, they never chattered to each other. These two were always the first to arrive in the morning, and the last to leave. They probably did not go far away, and slept in the trees close behind. Another regular visitor who arrived on his own and had his own spot in a tree to the left of the mothers, was 'Pink-ears', an adult male whose sparse hair allowed his pink skin to show through in a number of places, and who sported an enormous pair of floppy ears. A fourth early arrival was usually 'Cheeky Charlie', an adolescent who would come right out on to the edges of the branches overlooking the estate and though he often spotted us behind our inadequate coffee bush hides, never ran away, but peered and stared at us and moved to get a better view. Of these four only the two mothers arrived together, the two males came singly at different times, but all seemed to come from a sleeping place fairly close by.

As the sun began to clear the mist from the treetops, excited calls came from a finger of forest which lay away to the east along the river and, getting louder and closer, three large mature adult males bounded along, hitting trees, stamping and hollering as they approached the spot where the four were feeding. As they arrived and clambered up there was always some commotion in the trees which died down after a minute or two, as the adult males settled down to feeding in their favourite places. These males never remained for more than half an hour. Other choruses came from about a mile to the west, from the large part of the Siba forest proper, and these four males answered, eventually making off towards them. The mothers on the other hand, with Pink Ears, when they had finished their early morning feed, used to retreat towards the river where other chimps, among them

some other females, were feeding on a swampy 'Igeria' patch.
These were regular visitors, but each day of the first week and,
from time to time after that there were other individuals not seen
before and not recognized again. Thus, if these chimps all belonged to one group, then it was not a socially compact unit –
it did not sleep in one area, did not come or go in the same
direction, did not have the same daily routines, and was not
always composed of the same individuals.

The only way to find out if certain chimps always associated,
together, was by recognizing individuals. This was a simple
thing to do when we had the good luck to find a fruiting tree
with a group including it in its round of visits for a number of
days, as was described above. A good vantage point could be
chosen while the chimps were away, and positions taken up before
their arrival; the visitors each day were then described and compared with those of all the previous days. But the majority of our
days were 'jungle-bashing' days in which we tracked calls and
caught glimpses of bits of chimps high up in the trees, and could
never be certain of the identity of any individual. We had, however, seen enough to know that if chimps had permanent groups
they were loosely organized ones, in which small bands of twos
threes, fours, or fives travelled through the forest, meeting and
joining others, splitting up and going various ways. We knew
that large and noisy groups assembled when the sources of food
were concentrated, as in the fig season, and that when fruit was
scarce or widely scattered, the chimps made little noise, and were
found foraging singly or dispersed in twos and threes. We had
obtained no evidence of 'families' – there had never been any sign
of particular males associating with particular mothers; on the
contrary, mothers tended to keep together. Perhaps they did this
for the sake of each other's company, or perhaps they sought
extra safety in numbers. At all events, we found that these groups
of mothers with their young were extremely difficult to find and
observe in our forest conditions. For mothers were cautious and
suspicious. If one of them noticed a chance movement or a flashing lens, without waiting to ascertain what the cause of the
unusual stimulus was, off they all clambered with offspring
clasped to their bellies, and silently they were lost along the maze
of chimp tracks. Another difficulty was finding them in the first

place, for they were in general far less vociferous than the other adults, often staying in one patch of trees for hours or even days at a time, and not advertising their presence, except by very occasional little barks or squeals. Thus it was far more difficult for us to take a bearing and track off towards them. However, sometimes we struck lucky, and when we did get a few hours' good observations of a party of mothers and babies it was well worth the trouble.

For example, over Easter we had some real good fortune. We had been having a bad time as groups seemed very small, and were always moving about, food being scarce. One day near the end of April we had more or less given up for the day, having heard few calls, and having had no success tracking those. Manueri had run out of 'posho', and it was time we drove to the mill as the Land-Rover was in need of petrol and oil. So we set off on the seven-mile drive along the bumpy track. We were just negotiating the slippery muddy wooden bridge over the Kamirambwa river when Manueri shouted, "Soko mutu!" so suddenly that I braked and nearly ditched us into the water. We followed his pointing finger and there, incredibly, just by the roadside, in a huge sprawling fig tree, were at least a score of chimps feeding nonchalantly in full view! We thought they might leave when they saw us watching, and one or two did, but most remained, giving us no more than an occasional glance. The best explanation for this is that the chimps knew the road was human territory and that therefore humans on it did not present a 'threat'. In the forest, it is different; there humans are on animal territory and are therefore suspect. This theory was proved when, on one occasion, we tried moving closer to some 'tame' roadside chimps by entering the forest a little way towards them, whereupon they hurriedly left.

So we sat down casually on the murram, and started taking notes. There were four mothers in the tree. Two had quite small infants, of two years old or less and one of these was that rare but not unknown freak, a ginger-haired baby, ginger-coloured all over except for its face, which was sandy brown. Another mother had a small infant and a larger one of three or four years. The fourth had what we estimated to be a three-year-old. In addition there was a young adolescent female who might have been the

elder offspring of one of the mothers. Also in the tree were two
other adult females and an old grandma with a bald rump, grey
hair and a rheumaticky walk. A big powerful male was there at
first, and we thought perhaps he was looking after the females,
but he soon swung off with a hoot in answer to calls from farther
away, and we saw no more of him.

A delightful panorama of childish play now ensued. One of
the infants was playing with the three-year-old juvenile. The
juvenile stood up on all fours and the infant scrambled on its
back. Then the infant swung underneath to hang below the
juvenile's belly. They were obviously playing at 'mothers and
babies'. The juvenile put an arm round the infant but the infant
scrambled away and started jumping up and down on top of the
juvenile which now lay down. As the infant (or 'toto') swung
above the juvenile, the juvenile reached up and plonked a kiss
on its tiny bottom! Frankie kept saying "ah!"; it really was very
human and amusing. Later the other toto and juvenile and the
adolescent all joined in and played a chasing game, swinging,
falling, running; for half an hour they kept this up. At one
point one of the juveniles was being chased up a branch by a toto,
and the juvenile kept stamping on the reaching hands of the
infant below! When the mothers decided to leave later in the
afternoon, the youngsters were still playing, and as they left, the
adolescent female popped one of the infants beneath her and
carried it off in place of the mother.

Very young infants, of six months or less, remain nestled close
to the mother or swing just above her. When she moves, the tiny
baby clings below her belly and if it is very small it is difficult to
spot. At about a year, it is becoming more adventurous, and plays
and does acrobatics on the branches close by its mother. Later
still, in the next few years, it will ride on her back, 'piggy-back'
style, though if frightened, or when she travels fast, it will revert
to the belly position. Mothers are usually tolerant of the antics of
small infants, as they explore the environment and test their own
capabilities. We once watched a baby dancing up and down on
its mother's head, clinging to a small overhanging branch and
another time saw one swinging round and round her neck while
she attempted to feed! Chimpanzee mothers tend, rather like
human ones, to herd together, presumably on the basis of com-

mon interest, in groups of two to five mothers. The offspring then form active play-groups.

One day in early July we were able to test a theory we were developing. We had been watching large groups of chimps feeding in some swampy patches of forest in the Siba, rather south of the main forest, where some 'Igerias' had been ripe. Then one day, we set off as usual to the swamps only to find that, in bands of two or three, our chimps were leaving the swamps and crossing the road eastwards towards the big block of Budongo. All morning this was going on. As a party crossed, it gave loud calls, sometimes answered by those still to cross or those ahead. They did not all cross in one place but in several different ones along a stretch of road about a mile long. Manueri, Frankie, and I spaced ourselves out, and recorded and counted each group we saw. Later Africans and sawmill employees came to us and told us that still other parties were crossing at points of the road we could not cover. Leaving Frankie on the roadside to watch for developments, Manueri and I went in after one large group and tracked it north-eastwards until late afternoon. Calls came from all directions, those ahead, those behind, those on either side, but somehow all the chimps were bearing in the same direction. It seemed that rather than follow a particular route, chimps followed the direction of the calls and drums of those who went first. We lost track of the leaders, however; they seemed to be travelling fast deep into Budongo. Back on the road we counted up those we had seen or knew to have crossed during the morning. We counted between twenty and thirty, and among all of these we knew of only one definite mother and infant. Yet when we had been watching these selfsame chimp groups in the swamps, there had been many mothers and babies. Had they been left behind? Why had they not left with the others now that fruit was becoming scarce in the swamps?

Next morning at dawn we returned to the swamps and listened for calls as the sun slowly appeared. We heard a very few calls and crept cautiously into the forest. They were not far away, coming from one of our well-known Igeria patches. Nevertheless, it always takes longer than one could believe possible to get through forest cautiously and quietly and it was nine-twenty a.m. before we saw and heard the branches rustling ahead. We sat down unwilling to go farther, for if, as we suspected, these calls might be coming from the mothers and babies left behind by the males and other females, then we had to be ultra-careful. Manueri leant back against a shadowy tree trunk and became invisible, his dirty old jacket and black skin merging with the forest. But his eyes searched upwards, his head moving slightly to see beyond and through the leaves and branches. Frankie and I made sure there were covering canopies of leafy branches between us and the tree ahead where we could see the branches moving, and gently raised our binoculars to our eyes, elbows on raised knees, ready for a long wait. A slight chuckle from Manueri's direction made me turn towards him reproachfully. He pointed with his eyes, a big grin on his face. I focused in the direction he indicated and suddenly a tiny unsuspecting toto came into my field of view. He had been left to amuse himself, so he was running through his repertoire of acrobatics. He was hanging by both arms from a slender branch and bicycling gaily with his legs. Then up he swung his feet, gripped the branch, and let go with his hands, looking round and round, surveying the world from this new angle. Momentarily tiring, he disappeared upwards, but in a minute reappeared and encored the same performance. We timed seven minutes of his solo acrobatics while we watched. Panning the binoculars upwards to where the toto had gone, I could just make out a large black stationary form, no doubt the mother, feeding and glancing towards the toto. Suddenly he gave soft "ee, ee" sounds and looked upwards to the right of his mother. Into view leapt another toto, just slightly older, perhaps three years, and running towards number one he grasped him, and the two of them rolled about hugging each other, front to front for some minutes. I don't know how they managed not to fall off the branches!

They left our view and for a while we could see nothing, only vague branch movements; then we caught sight of them again. This time, they were having a wrestling match, heads low, pummelling each other. This was great fun. Manueri thought it all a tremendous joke and murmured "sasa watu" – "just like people". But there were more fun and games to come. After losing them again among the leaves, we rediscovered our totos, with a *third* one now, sliding down a long swinging liana – the sort used by Tarzan to leap through the jungle – and then, funniest of all, racing back up through the branches simply to slide down again! Once there were two closely following upon each other, and the top one kicked out at the one underneath. They moved out of view and we, with aching eyes, decided to eat our sandwiches. During lunch the adults moved closer to us in the Igeria trees, and one, a wary, pregnant old female, must have spotted something, and we just managed to grab our binoculars in time to see them all leaving. In the tree had been three females and one pregnant female, three 'totos' and a young adolescent chimp. When they left it was in the direction of a few soft calls heard earlier in the morning, perhaps some other mothers and babies.

It now seemed that our theory was being proved right. This was that the bands of adult males, often accompanied by childless females and the older adolescent chimps, formed the most active and mobile groups that we saw. Mothers, and other interested females, on the other hand, tended to band together, and remained longer on familiar trees, making less noise. Working on these ideas, and alive to any clues which might help us to see *how* this type of social organization might have helped the chimpanzees survive in their evolution, we tried to fit in some of the other facts. Firstly, there was the prodigiously loud noise that chimps made when feeding in a tree with masses of fruit, in contrast with their silence when food was scarce; and secondly there was the fact that the bands of active and mobile adult males hooted noisily and, especially, drummed as they moved through the forest. What if the males, powerful and untrammelled by young-sters, were the *food-finders*, announcing their progress through the forest by hooting and drumming, and their success when they found a good tree by creating a tremendous hullaballoo; where-upon first the other adults and then the groups of mothers moved to the new area, having wasted no effort hunting about the forest, but relying on the males for guidance? It was a good theory and we worked on it; as time went by new facts emerged and con-firmed it, and to this day we believe that this is the solution which chimpanzees have developed to tackle the problems of forest life.

CHAPTER NINE

Gorillas

Another kind of ape lives in Uganda – the gorilla. Why not try and see some while we were so close by? The more we thought about it, the better the idea seemed to be. Finally we fixed a date, in July, when we would down tools, give Semei and Manueri a couple of weeks off, and head south to gorilla-land. And in due course that date arrived.

We weren't just 'going to see the gorillas'. What we hoped for was a *contrast*, chimp versus gorilla, which might help us to see the chimpanzee's particular adaptations more clearly, for the gorilla, superficially just a larger version of the chimpanzee, is, in fact, very different in many ways. We knew something of these differences from reading and from hearing about George Schaller's excellent study of these mountain gorillas, then just completed. Apart from the question of size – gorilla males are fully three times as big as chimpanzee males, and females are twice as big – there was the matter of social organization. Unlike the Budongo chimpanzees, we knew from Schaller's studies that gorillas live in fairly small, permanent groups, the members of each group keeping in contact with each other at all times, and we knew that each group was led by a single big silver-backed male. *Why* this outstanding difference from the chimpanzees, with their loose, dispersed society and lack of permanent groups and leaders?

Schaller had shown the gorilla to be mainly a terrestrial creature – big males in particular very rarely climb trees. And together with this goes the ground diet of gorillas – pithy stems, leaves, roots, and bark being their main source of nourishment, while fruits provide no more than a supplement. How different from the chimpanzees, happiest when they can gorge themselves on fruits for hours at a time, high in the treetops. This difference of food habits was, we felt, of fundamental importance and might help to explain other problems such as the difference in social organization.

There were other intriguing questions: Why does the gorilla soil its nest with dung every night, while the chimpanzee keeps its nest scrupulously clean, performing its natural functions over the edge? And why is the chimpanzee one of the noisiest, most vocal creatures in creation, while gorillas are quiet most of the time? And finally the most teasing question of all – why should gorillas have a morose, sullen, placid temperament, while chimpanzees are volatile, lively, and excitable? The more we thought about it, the more we realized how different the two species were.

Turning these questions over in our minds, we drove along the damp red murram road towards Fort Portal, the first town on our southward route. It was now the wet season in this part of the country, no bush fires, no dust trail. If only we could see those gorillas! We had met people who had gone on this very quest without success, who had returned tired and disappointed but vowing to try again, such is the magnetic attraction of these giant apes.

From Fort Portal we took the road down into Ankole district, a bare country of hills and plains, with every here and there a huge herd of cattle, lean but with giant curved horns: the famous Ankole cattle, more beautiful than any others in the world. How they managed to support the huge weight of those horns we often wondered: it was a thought which, quite obviously, had never entered their lovely heads. Here the cattle are not as sacred as they are in India, but neither do they exist simply for food – in addition, they are regarded as a source of wealth and are used in bride-wealth transactions. As a result they are left to reproduce among themselves and only barren cows are fattened for killing and eating. We saw the slim herd-boys as we drove through the treeless plain, holding painted gourds from which they drank milk to slake their thirst.

We camped in Ankole, where the land was rising a little towards the mountains farther west; that evening three herdsmen came and sat with us, each carrying a long stick; we could not talk to them. At night it grew bitterly cold and we shivered in our sleeping bags. We were already breakfasting as the sun broke through the mist around the hills next day, and were soon on our way through the tinkle of African cow bells heading towards

N

Kigezi District. What a contrast it was! Rolling mountainous country, cultivated in terraces all the way up and down its steep slopes, no cattle here but dark fertile soil, a happy atmosphere above the subsistence level, bee-hives long and slim hanging from the trees, flowers, and the road always climbing up ahead, far up into a further range of hills. The people by the roadside were cheerful and had patterned mats for sale. They wore dust-coloured sheets tied around their necks or under one arm, in contrast with the more ragged appearance of the people on our home-ground up in Bunyoro, or in Ankole we had just passed through. There too, in Ankole, the men all carried hunting spears; here they carried lovely baskets full of vegetables on their heads. We bought a basket for a shilling; it was a work of art.

After a long winding mountainous road we arrived in Kabale, a sleepy town in the midday heat with identical Indian shops in a long row down either side of the street. From Kabale on to little Kisoro township, six thousand feet up, on the Ruanda border. Here we were welcomed by Walter Baumgartel who runs the world-famous gorilla safari-lodge 'Travellers Rest'. Situated just inside the no-man's-land between Uganda and Ruanda, it is a delightful cluster of gaily decorated and comfortable lodges, and the host himself is the most hospitable and friendliest man alive. Above Travellers Rest loom the volcanoes where the gorillas live, Mount Muhavura, 13,547 feet, the nearest, Mount Mgahinga next, and in the distance Mount Sabinio. As we sat on our verandah in the evening it seemed unreal that somewhere on those vast conical slopes, now dimming behind a purple evening mist, some great apes were snatching a final feed and making their nests before retiring for the night, and it seemed even more unreal that next day we should be going up there ourselves. The volcanoes seemed more like a picture on the wall, not something that could be travelled over. But later at supper we met a man who had been up that very day and glimpsed them; it was the first time someone had done so in several weeks, a good omen.

During the evening we were entertained with exquisite African music by Sawa-sawa, an old Batwa beggar who for a shilling sings and plays on a stringed instrument at Travellers Rest. His pygmoid tribe is a servant tribe (or was until the recent revolution), under the tall, superior Watutsi, and the ballads he plays are in an ancient Ruanda tongue known only to these servant bards. His eyes looked wistful as he played, he seemed to sing of love; and then the note changed and he danced about on his old legs, thrusting, thrusting with an imaginary spear, shouting and guffawing and crouching back in fear: was it the hunt or war? Soon he was quiet again and strumming a new and infinitely subtle rhythm.

Most of the people here in Kisoro are neither Batwa nor Watutsi, but a middle group, middle in stature and status: the Wahutu, gay people, whose women wear dozens of gold coloured bangles round their arms and legs, and are among the most beautiful in all Africa.

Trade had had its ups and downs over the past months, Baumgartel told us, but this evening was certainly an up. Since the Congo's independence economic conditions there had deteriorated, the Congo franc had steadily lost value, and, the Belgian traders having left, vast stocks of certain commodities such as coffee and tea had accumulated inside the stricken land. These, it seems, were now being bartered for much-needed products from outside, such as salt and bottled beer, on a lorry for lorry basis. The profits being made by anyone bartering a load of beer for a load of coffee kept trade busy. And not only coffee but gold was being found inside the sacks, gold which was leaving the Congo fast before it slipped from the Belgian miners' hands into those of the authorities. So every lorry, and there were a dozen or more each day, was being searched at the customs post, for this way out of Congo, via Ruanda, was one of the major smuggling routes. This meant a delay of hours or even days for the crews, who seemed to be mainly Italians, and they were thus seeking shelter for the night; 'Smugglers' Rest' might have been a better name for the hotel that night, one felt.

On the subject of gorillas, Baumgartel had sad stories to tell. A fine male had recently been found dead of wounds by Reuben Rwangzire, the chief gorilla guide, and he suspected it was the work of a powerful and bloodthirsty leopard. But, far more ominous than this natural disaster, one result of Congo's Independence and the turbulent social changes in Ruanda was tha regulations preventing the movement of Ruanda pastoralists from taking their herds up the mountain-sides into gorilla country were being ignored successfully for the first time in many years. This encroachment by men and cattle was pushing the lower limit of gorilla habitat farther up the mountains daily. And finally Baumgartel suspected that in Ruanda and the Congo gorillas were being caught, dead or alive, and sold through secret channels to zoos and museums in the civilized world. The net result of all this was that only one group of gorillas now visited the Uganda side of Muhavura, a group of five, the one which had been seen that very day. We should have to find this little group of survivors.

We set off early next morning to make arrangements with our trackers. We met the great Reuben, but he could not accompany us as he was off to Entebbe next day to receive a medal from the Governor, on behalf of Her Majesty Queen Elizabeth, in recognition of his services to wildlife conservation. He arranged for the two remaining trackers, Peter and 'Muzee', to take us, and provided us with six porters to carry our gear. We were taking with us a week's stores, and would camp in Baumgartel's huts on the saddle between Mount Muhavura and Mount Mgahinga. Early in the afternoon, amid wishes of good luck, we set off. Ahead marched the porters with their loads, while the guides kept us company. It was a steady slope, but there was a good path and it was less cruel than the Ruwenzori had been, up above Chapman's Farm. We were now on a track leading over this mountain saddle and into Ruanda, a natural pass which had been used for centuries, most recently by displaced Watutsi fleeing the wrath of their former Wahutu subjects, who threatened to cut off the tall men's legs to bring them down to size. Everlasting flowers were common, and as we climbed and the sounds of humans died away below us we were aware of the pleasantly bracing air and the overall silence, as if few birds and insects lived up here. At ten thousand feet, after a four-thousand-foot climb which took a mere one and a quarter hours, we saw the metal and thatch huts of the camp where Schaller had stayed before us, while making his study of the gorillas in this area. We paid off our porters, and started setting up camp. Evening came and with it a cold wind. Clouds swept down from the peak of Muhavura, three thousand five hundred feet above us. We grew desperately cold. We tried lighting a fire in our hut but the smoke was so thick we had to crouch at floor level in order to breathe, our eyes streamed and

our throats pricked, and then that was no use. The three men
(two trackers and a camp guard) must have spotted our antics,
for in no time they had made a fire out in the open, a big blazing
bonfire, and put a couple of wicker screens on the windward side
of it. Sitting inside those screens we toasted ourselves as the
night closed in around us and when at last we plunged out into
the cold and made for our camp-beds, we kept on all our clothes
inside a feather-filled sleeping bag, covered with a thick blanket –
and still our feet were cold.

The next morning was dank and misty and we could not see
downwards into the plains at all, or upwards to Muhavura. We
set off about eight a.m. and first the guides led us downwards
along a steep track through the bamboo forest, which here covers
the mountain in a broad horizontal belt around the ten thousand
foot contour. At nine-thirty we picked up the track of two days
ago – a flattened trail left by these enormous heavy creatures as
they move slowly along, with dung at intervals along it and the
occasional bamboo peelings. We now began a similar kind of
journey to that described by Alan Moorehead, up the near-
vertical sides of gulleys, along ridges, down again into a gulley,
for this is a jagged volcanic cone, with longitudinal fissures
running downwards from the summit. As we toiled along we
heard golden monkeys but could not see them in the dense
bamboo, saw droppings which could have been leopard, and
bigger ones, though not at all fresh, of elephant. Elephant here?
Yes, they assured us, elephants sometimes climbed to the very
summit of Muhavura. Well, if an elephant could do it then so
could we.

At ten-thirty, while still in the bamboo, we came across the
gorillas' sleeping place of the previous night, four nests close to
each other in the tops of bamboos, and one near by on the ground
which must have belonged to the old male; as we expected, it
contained dung. Now we emerged from the bamboo into a land-
scape, none the less jagged, of giant *lobelias* and *senecios*, where we
continued sliding and slipping down, and heaving ourselves up
on roots and tufts of grass which naturally came out half the
time so that we had to start again. We were by now rather dead,
I fear, to the skilful tracking which was keeping us on the
gorillas' path; at times we wondered whether we could hope to

catch up with them, our progress was so slow. But the trackers were confident.

After three and a half hours of following, Peter suddenly signed us to listen and we heard a crack as a branch was snapped ahead of us. We scrambled higher and peered into the gulley ahead, and there on the opposite side below us we saw a splendid black gorilla looking at us. It watched us a while and then went on feeding and moved up the side of the gulley opposite looking like a great black bear. Then came another from the bottom, this one a female with a baby on her back. She too looked at us, transferred the baby to her belly, and pulled herself up and out of sight behind the foliage. Next came the big male, a huge gorilla with a silver back. He looked at us and roared and barked at us angrily over the gulley. Then he went up a little way until he was hidden and must have stayed there and watched us all the time for he still barked, roared, and beat his chest from time to time, making a strange hollow knocking sound. He also made slapping and thudding noises. While this was going on, two more smaller gorillas came into view and both walked up the same route slowly, after having a good look at us.

Altogether we had been watching for half an hour and were conscious of our extreme good luck. As the minutes had been ticking by we had felt something of the grandeur of these giants in their mountain fastness, but more the extreme aloofness of them; the male had conveyed his power to us, and the rest had shown themselves to be curious and dignified. Also, we had established for sure that there was a baby in the group, perhaps two years old, making the total number six. We had been exceptionally well placed for observation: above the gorillas and at a good distance from them. We now started to return to camp, exhausted but elated by our success at the first attempt. Peter explained to us that the gorillas were now going up the mountain, he doubted whether we would see them again.

Nevertheless, next morning found us on those jagged slopes again, crawling up and up, higher far than we had been the day before, up until we reached the new nesting site, four nests in the trees and one below, as on the previous night. Up the track went, headed apparently straight for the summit of Muhavura. This was an advantage: we were moving along a ridge without

having to cross gulleys all the time. Up and up we went, out of
the *senecio* zone and into a higher one of giant heather – small
gaunt trees with bilious-looking lichen hanging from the branches
in streamers, steadily step by step picking our way along the
ridge under a blue sky with only one cloud forming around the
summit, which was now a mere two thousand feet above us. At
11.25 the trackers heard feeding noises; we went on a few steps
and immediately the silence of the mountain, so far this morning
broken only by the dull slow padding of our feet and our panting
breaths, was shattered by a terrible roar, long and furious like a
mad dog's, and we heard a thump as of rapidly approaching
pelting feet. Ahead of me the two trackers turned and ran back
down the mountain, I too turned and shouted to Frankie to run
down, we all four tumbled down the mountain with extreme haste
and no grace and came to rest below by a big rock, whereupon
we all burst out laughing with relief. Not even Peter, who was
in the lead, had seen the big male as he charged, probably he
hadn't stopped to look. We remembered now, objectively, that
this charge of the gorilla is no more than a display, rarely leading
to attack, so that one can in fact stand still and watch it; on this
occasion the combination of surprise, shock, and an instinct in all
of us, telling us strongly to get out of it, had triumphed. But then
we recalled that this particular gruff old male was known to
attack by throttling and had twice got hold of Reuben in this
way, and I, for one, was glad we had been cowards enough to run.

Above us the cloud still lingered around Muhavura's volcanic
rim and silence reigned absolute in the mountain air. Below, the
sun was on the mountain slopes and among the ridges of greens
and browns we saw a tiny silver speck: our own camp. Three
hours later, when we returned, the guard greeted us with relief;
he had heard the roar more than a mile away over the trees.

That afternoon we sent him down to Kisoro to summon the
porters; we had accomplished our objective and now saw that
the gorillas were moving out of range. Up they would go, over
the mountain's shoulder and down into Ruanda on the far side.
If only we could have warned them of the dangers across the
border! Next evening we were telling Baumgartel all we had
seen, and the day after that were on our way north, through the
Impenetrable Forest, the only spot in Uganda where both gorillas

and chimpanzees are known to occur together. And as we bumped around the precipitous tree-covered gulleys of this forest on the only road which cuts through it, we imagined the two species around us among the trees and got back to thinking about those striking differences which had puzzled us.

There was the difference in food habits, and we now saw the importance of one specific point. The gorilla can find its food almost anywhere. It spends more time deciding which of the available foods growing all around it to eat, than where to find any food at all. This is because pithy stems, roots, etc., are found scattered about everywhere; what is more, they are available everywhere all the year round. Gorillas thus feed, as we saw them do, by working their way in a compact group along a rather imprecise route at a slow pace, eating a little here and a little there as they go. When they do make particular journeys to particular feeding areas, it is because the food in these areas is preferable, not because there is no food elsewhere. For the fruit-eating chimpanzee this is not the case: we had been struck by the overwhelming importance of the whereabouts of ripe fruits in determining the pattern of movement and distribution of the Budongo chimpanzees. They had a flexible social organization because they needed it in order to be able to exploit the fruit supply, now concentrated in one spot, now scattered all over the forest. Whereas, in theory, gorillas *could* go around as chimps do, there is no advantage to be gained in doing so. Indeed, one can see the advantage of being in a group with a big male leader to provide protection – an advantage which chimpanzees have had to forgo completely. This, then, was how food habits had helped to shape the social organization of each species.

Then there was the fact that the gorilla was quiet and the chimpanzee vociferous. Apart from the terrifying roar and the barking and chest-beating of the adult male, the gorillas we had seen, and those described by Schaller, were quiet animals with a number of subdued vocalizations. In other words, noise is the gorilla's technique of threatening an enemy, and is largely the prerogative of adult males. There is none of the wild chorusing of chimpanzees, whose hullaballoo may be connected with threat behaviour, but, we thought, was primarily a distance signal enabling chimpanzees all over the forest to home on good food sources. Now, after our trip, it was obvious to us that gorillas would have no use for such noisy chorusing, there being no special areas of good food. A fascinating detail drove home to us the importance of vocalizations in chimpanzees as opposed to gorillas: the chimp's ears are much bigger for its size and stick out much further from the head than the gorilla's.

The temperamental difference between the two species also now seemed to be a logical one and to fall into the general framework. Gorillas travel along slowly, they rarely get excited or worked up about anything. Chimpanzees, in contrast, move along the forest floor at a great pace; the males, in particular, cover more ground each day than do gorillas. They hoot and drum as they move along, and when they find a fruiting tree their enthusiasm knows no bounds. This kind of boisterous behaviour could only be exhibited by a species with an underlying 'volatile' temperament and so this is the way chimpanzee temperament has evolved. Gorillas, on the other hand, have never stood to gain from excitability in everyday life; their temperament has thus become placid and their only expression of excitement comes in their threatening displays.

But what about the dung? What explanation could we find in terms of temperament or social organization or food habits? Wasn't it just that the gorilla was a slothful, dirty creature, while the chimpanzee had developed a primitive toilet sense? Why look further into this rather messy problem? Why muck about with dung? We couldn't help it. When we had found the gorillas' nesting site, on our first day, we had been struck not by the pile of dung in the big male's ground nest, which we had expected, but by the fact that, although pushed down by the weight of his body (some three to four hundred pounds) it still retained its basic shape. Thinking back to the gorillas we had seen, I remembered them as clean-looking, glossy-haired animals. And Schaller in his book remarked on the fact that gorillas are not dirtied by lying on their dung. With chimpanzees it is different. Their food is less fibrous and so their droppings are soft, loose, and often messy. If chimpanzees lay in their dung all night it would cling to their fur and act as a focus of infection. So, in the course of chimpanzee evolution, natural selection may well have favoured those with hygienic habits and eliminated those with

unhygienic ones, while gorillas have been more fortunate –
despite their apparently dirty habits, their diet makes it difficult
for them to be unhygienic!

So we theorized as we drove the long journey back to Bunyoro.
The road jogged us mercilessly along every hot hour, our equipment clattered around in the back of the Land-Rover, attractive
hills or dull flat landscapes passed slowly by on either side. On
the second day we were forced to a standstill by a great storm
which blotted out everything for half an hour and left the red
road steaming ahead of us. Steadily we made our way northwards, to Fort Portal and beyond, and were back on our beloved
verandah by nightfall of the second day, with the welcoming calls
of chimpanzees in our ears.

CHAPTER TEN

Back to Budongo

Before we broke our study to go to the gorillas, we had seen four seasons go by, the fig, lean, 'Ngrube', and 'Igeria' seasons. We had obtained excellent evidence that chimpanzees did not live in permanent groups, and we had developed certain theories about the nature of chimp society and the function of the choruses. But, and we felt this keenly, we had not yet obtained satisfactory data relating to the problem of *which* chimpanzees went *where*, i.e. whether or not a particular number of chimps, however loosely bound together, occupied a given area of forest only and did all their wandering around in it. Such an area, known as a 'range' is very common in animals of all kinds, and we suspected that ranges existed for our chimpanzees too, as we most often heard them in certain areas and more rarely in others. But since we lacked proof of which chimpanzees were in fact calling in these areas we could not be sure of whether they kept to ranges or not. Of one thing we were sure, namely that the ranges, if they existed, were very large, for there were no small, compact areas of a square mile or so where chimpanzees could be found at all times. When one species of fruit tree ripened they were feeding on this; when it was replaced by another in a different part of the forest they moved accordingly, so the range, if it existed, must be extensive enough to contain a number of trees of each major food species in order to provide a year-round supply of food.

While we had been away in Kigezi, we had formulated in rough a plan of campaign which ought to help us get the necessary facts to answer our outstanding problem. On returning to the forest we would hire some of the wandering unemployed in our region to be 'chimp-spotters' – about six of them, we thought; these would be placed at strategic listening points and their daily reports should give us a clearer picture of the *total* pattern of movement of all the chimpanzees in our study area. For our major

difficulty to date had been that by following one group we were
forced to neglect and lose track of all the others. We should now
have several pairs of ears and eyes in the forest like a network of
survey posts, and we should, in theory at least, be able to track
several chimpanzee movements without actually following any
of them. So now, back in Budongo, we began putting out feelers
among the local people to try and get some good 'chimp-
spotters', and in this Manueri helped a good deal.

Meantime we planned to continue jungle-bashing as usual.
July was now well advanced and, although we did not know it
yet, a new season had begun; gone forever were our days in the
Siba swamps. The first thing we noticed on our return was the
extraordinary loudness of the calling which seemed to be coming
from the forest just below the house. All our first evening at
home it continued: were they welcoming us back? Looking down
towards the noisy forest next morning at dawn, we were staggered
to find the treetops we knew so well full of chimpanzees. I still
remember the strange feeling of standing, snake-bite serum in
pocket, camera and binoculars slung, Manueri at our side with
his panga, bag packed full of sandwiches, water, and plastic macs,
anxious to get back on the trail after our break, only to be faced
with this unpredicted turn of events: we could now do our
observing from the verandah!

Manueri, despite his fortnight's holiday, was quick off the
mark. "Sisi nakwenda, sokomutu nakuja," he laughed – "We
go away, the chimpanzees come," adding seriously, "Mimi
nafikiri kama sisi nafuta-futa kibrani, yote tatoroka mbale sana," –
"I think that if we go down and search for them in the forest,
they will all flee a long way away." I nodded in agreement with
his second point; we should certainly find out less by going down
the hill and hacking our way in to these chimpanzees than by
staying put. For the first time I got out the 60× magnification
telescope lent us by Dollonds of London, and mounted it on the
verandah. Manueri hung around for a bit, politely, but was soon
up in his hut lying on his back and smoking – the halcyon days
had come. We took notes and watched.

Below the house we distinguished, with the telescope, four
adult males feeding together in one tree and in another a mixed
group of seven chimpanzees of all ages and sexes. The trees were

'Musisi' or *Maesopsis*, the colonizing species of Budongo. We had read in a book by Eggeling that this species was a favourite food of the chimpanzee but had never, so far, found them in it. Now we could see that each tree with chimps was festooned with thousands of tiny yellow or black fruits, depending on the state of ripeness, while other nearby trees were still unripe and covered in blobs of green. Perhaps Eggeling had watched them on these very trees from the spot where we were now standing, when he had lived here.

We kept our things ready to go down if they disappeared, but they stayed. As always, new chimps came and others left. Our four males were, we felt sure, a group we had seen together on previous occasions and which we called the 'royal clan' because they were so relaxed; this group seemed to be more permanent than most chimpanzee groups, although we could not be sure whether the four stayed together all the time; they might split up and meet again. By now we were esconced in camp chairs with our feet on the table and bush jackets abandoned for cooler clothes, with Semei laughingly turning up with mugs of tea at regular intervals. Information of all sorts was pouring in. For a start, we saw one of our males make a 'day-bed' at mid-morning and settle down on his back in it for a snooze – he appeared not to go to sleep but simply to want a rest, for he lay there yawning and stretching in the sunshine (the nest was right at the top of a tree), and after an hour or so of this, got up quite casually and left. In addition, from our new position above canopy level we could see anything from five to a dozen chimpanzees at the same time and observe their interactions with each other as, one by one, they stopped feeding and either left the tree or started to groom one another. We saw a big old grey-backed male, so old his face was lean and showed the skull beneath, grooming and being groomed by a spry young female having an early oestrus. We watched them groom each other, and then the grooming stopped, the old male collected a few branches underneath him for comfort, and sat gazing into space over the treetops, his young lady seemingly forgotten. She sat nearby scratching, and nibbling a desultory bite of fruit here and there, then walked away.

These chimpanzees called from time to time, their wild music going out over the trees and provoking a response from other groups deeper in the forest. For all of one day we recorded every call, its time, the direction it came from, whether or not there was any drumming; from this information we were able to plot groups of chimps moving down among the trees as the bearing of their calls crept degree by degree across the compass dial. We got better evidence than ever before for our theory that the calling of chimpanzees feeding busily up aloft acts both as a magnet and as a beacon for wandering groups of chimpanzees in the forest below.

By late morning the 'royal clan' had left for pastures new but some of the others were still there. We lunched to their sporadic music. In the afternoon they moved slowly to neighbouring trees where we could still see them. It was wonderful to be able to watch their agility in the branches, unhurried and yet powerful and fast, bending the smaller branches under them, climbing tree trunks that rose vertically for a hundred feet with an ease which really brought home to us what it is to be a chimpanzee; to look around one at ground level and see the world not, human-fashion, as a number of paths *between* the trees, but as a number of paths *up* the trees, and, once up aloft, to see each tree-crown near by as a field of branches in which to wander and pluck the choicest fruits.

For three days there were nearly always some chimps visible from our verandah; sometimes, too, blue monkeys and redtails came to feed on the 'Musisis' with them. The treetops where they fed were now beginning to look ravaged with hundreds of broken-off branch-stubs and dying leaves, and we got a good idea of the way in which chimpanzees help the spread of the *Maesopsis* tree, by depositing the stones (in their dung) in areas far from the parent tree, as they wander through the forest. Other species of animals also help the *Maesopsis* spread – the hornbills, the duikers, and the civet cat, for instance. But of these only the hornbills move regularly over such long distances as the chimpanzees, and they probably drop their stones before going far, which makes the chimpanzee the number one distributor of *Maesopsis* trees in the forest and ought, therefore, to make him the forester's friend, since *Maesopsis* is a valuable timber tree. But the forester is ungrateful, and is at the present time engaged in a

systematic attempt to kill off all the fig trees in the forest by a
massive tree-poisoning programme, since figs do not make good
timber; in so doing he will strike a blow at the chimpanzees,
which rely on figs during the early part of the year. It is a blow
which they may survive, being highly adaptable creatures, but
only in reduced numbers. They will have lost their favourite
food, the Mukunyu, and will have to try and find substitutes
during certain months; let us hope substitutes are available, for
no one knows. We fully acknowledge Uganda's need to continue
timber production; in an under-developed country there can be
no talk of wild-life survival where the survival of essential
industries is at stake. And yet – is it really necessary to kill off the
figs in order to benefit the mahoganies? According to Eggeling,
figs contribute greatly to soil fertility. While nothing is proven,
it is possible to suggest that the forest as a whole, and therefore
the mahoganies, might suffer if fig trees were exterminated. But
whether that is true or not, there is no doubt about the importance
of figs to the chimpanzees. The Forest Department is watching to
see the effects poisoning will have on chimpanzees, but it will be
very difficult for anyone not engaged full-time on the task to
notice a decline in their numbers. In the meantime, every day,
more trees in Budongo are being pumped with a mixture of diesel
oil and a hormone killer which prevents proper cell growth. *No
one* knows what the full effects of this poisoning programme will
be on the wild-life which at present abounds around the trees
and on them and underneath them. What we need are censuses of
the numbers of animals living in areas which have been poisoned;
the figures can then be compared with those for un-poisoned
areas of the same forest type. Let us hope that such work will be
started before the balance of plant and animal life in whole areas
of forest is irrevocably upset.

Getting back to the season of the 'Musisis' and to our verandah,
there was a quiet spell after the third day, with no chimps in
evidence, and we had evidence from our notebooks that throughout these three days they had been moving off towards the
south. We began trekking through the forest again. It was
strange, they had disappeared. We followed along the rim of the
Budongo Forest and came to the place where the main road
cuts between the Budongo and the Siba. Here Manueri found

fresh chimp tracks crossing the main road. We entered the Siba
from this new direction on Manueri's hypothesis. And there,
in the afternoon, we heard chimpanzees calling, miles away, deep
in the distant Siba, in the elephant-ridden part. If these were our
chimpanzees they could stay there; we would look for some
different ones. And for a few days we did. Then one dawn there
was calling from the south of Busingiro, loud strident calling
like the yelping of wild dogs; these were excited chimpanzees.
We went down into the forest and headed towards the music,
which was almost continuous. We soon realized that they were
coming towards us and coming fast. Drumming in great rolls
reverberated through the trees and every instant we expected to
see a black form in the bushes, see it pull up sharp and look at us
and dive off again into the darkness. The noise was now growing
fantastically loud and we could scarcely believe that it could get
louder, but it could and did. We began to feel that if this enormous
horde of approaching chimpanzees did bump into us it would be
just too bad for us – they sounded utterly lunatic in their extreme
frenzy of drumming and hooting. We stopped still by a tree
trunk, I comforted Frankie as best I could and Manueri peered
forwards with panga at the ready. All of a sudden we realized
that they were passing by us, we could have shouted out loud
and not made ourselves heard above the din; a few times something moved between the saplings but the noise of their voices
was so great that we heard no footsteps or rustling leaves. For a
minute or two this phenomenon, like a cyclone or a passing
express train, swept past us and then was gone, travelling north.
We looked at each other in bewilderment; none of us had so
much as glimpsed a chimpanzee, only seen the bushes moving
everywhere. As before with the gorillas, we laughed and spoke
out loudly in our relief after the awful mounting tension and
terrible climax. One thing we had learned: that the howling of a
mob of chimpanzees, whatever functions it may have in the
organizing of chimp society, is extremely intimidating to other
species in its path. This helped to answer a problem we had
often wondered about: why chimpanzees were so keen to
announce their whereabouts to all and sundry, including leopards.
It now seemed to us that any leopard caught in a mob of chimps
as we had been, would be more likely to retreat terrified into

13a. and b. Chimpanzees eating *Maesopsis*.

14. Adult male feeding.

a crotch than risk a plunge into that cauldron of screaming fury. Another mystery was cleared up too – how it was that we had in the past been able to hear chimpanzees over vast distances, which we had measured up to two full miles as the crow flies: we now felt that the noise we had heard, produced as it was by the combined lung power of some twenty or more chimpanzees, would carry a couple of miles with no trouble at all. Problem: what in heaven's name were they up to?

During the week after our return I had interviewed at least a dozen men, to select those who, I felt, were the best type for the job of 'chimp-spotting', for our new large-scale attack on the problem of chimp 'ranges'. After establishing that they knew what chimpanzees and their calls were like, by asking for an imitation (which most of the men were glad to provide), and weeding out those who lived too far away or whom Manueri disapproved of, I had selected six men who, starting the following Monday, were to be at certain fixed spots – 'strategic points' on chimpanzee routes or between areas thought by us to be possible chimp ranges – to keep their ears and eyes open for three hours after dawn and again for three hours before dusk, and report to us when we came to visit them on anything they might have seen or heard. It was ambitious stuff, and this, our first attempt at such a project in the heart of Africa, failed utterly; within the week we had fired every man. Not a single one of them consistently turned up on time or in the right place, when it rained they didn't come, or their bicycles let them down, or something. But word had got around about what we were looking for, and soon men were turning up on Busingiro Hill in a steady stream, presenting themselves for the jobs. Having learnt a few lessons from the first batch, I now inquired whether they were afraid of the forest, whether they minded being left alone in the forest for three hours, what they would do in the rain, did they want an advance? (If yes, I told them to go home.) It took time, but we ended up with four reliable men. They all had one quality in common – an extreme aloofness and independence of spirit, born, most probably, of prolonged suffering. There was Zacchariah, tall and lean with a domed, professorial head, a quiet-spoken man with a keen sense of fun, if you caught what he said. The second, Akijero, had left his wife and child in Hoima and

o

was wandering around Bunyoro asking for work; he had been away for three months and this was the first job he had found. Third was Amis, the sacked houseboy of a local European; he claimed to be an expert cook but according to his reference (which he could not read) was a kitchen-boy and a bad one, and the last was a smiling-faced, pock-marked local who lived on his own and went under the extraordinary name of 'Watu Hapana' which means 'no people': he certainly was lacking entirely in the social instinct but claimed the name had been given him at birth and not as a result of his behaviour. This, then, was the force with which we hoped to breach the final mystery of the chimpanzees, the problem of how big their 'tribes' were and how far the range of each 'tribe' extended. Amis and Zacchariah and Akijero came to live with Semei and Manueri. Watu Hapana stayed at home until he took to the job so warmly that he built himself a little hut at his allocated observation point, after which he worked up to twelve hours a day and became a fanatical source of information about the chimpanzees' latest movements and positions: he may have been 'no people' but he certainly was 'chimp'.

We were now obliged to make visits to our men at ten a.m. and at six-thirty p.m. for their reports and so for a while the old routine of jungle bashing came to an end and a new one took its place. During the period before ten a.m. and between eleven a.m. and the evening we now followed up any groups of chimpanzees located by the men or, if none seemed promising, stationed ourselves at a fifth observation point for the day, using the time available to work on our maps and plot the latest information. Akijero was walking up Track A as far as RP5; Amis was at the first river on the mill track; Zacchariah was half a mile along Track B; Watu Hapana was down by the Siba swamps. We ourselves observed from the road at the Budongo–Siba crossing point; we had the study area in our grip, sixteen square miles of forest in which we ought to be able to pick up any noisy chimpanzee group, locate it, and follow its progress.

In addition to our work of watching and analysing data as we sat at the roadside, we were kept busy greeting and replying to passing Africans, for this is no land of the curtly civil "good morning" or "good afternoon" and the false smile. The ritual,

repeated with every man and woman who came padding or
cycling up the road went something like this:

"Jambo" – "Hullo."

"Jambo."

"Habari?" – "What news?"

"Muzuri. Habari?" – "Good news. What is your news?"

"Muzuri tu" – "Only good."

"Poli kazi" – "Work slowly."

"Poli poli" – "Go steadily."

"Eh" – "Yes."

"Mmmm."

"Mmmm." (Out of earshot now.)

All spoken in quiet, sedate tones, fading with the last "mmmm"
into the African silence. There were variations on the ceremony.
For instance, inquiry might be made, after "muzuri tu", as to our
success in hearing chimpanzees, or we could inquire where a
man was going, or whence he had come, or if his fish was for
sale. If there was any conversation, one ended with "Kwaheri" –
"Good-bye."

The soft tones of the Africans' voices in greeting somehow
conveyed the tranquillity of their lives; more than this, the
complacent way the long ritual was delivered expressed their
whole fatalistic approach to life, and the steady pad-padding of
their feet on the red road drove this impression home. Here was
none of the white man's dash and verve; here was no belief in
progress; here, one felt, was life balanced in perfect equilibrium
with the earth, and the earth might even be no more than a
symbol of death.

Then, always, just as our minds were musing on imponderable
things, lulled no doubt by the heat and the constant drone of
insects in the trees, a black form would emerge at the roadside
thirty yards away – the head of a chimpanzee, standing on its
hind legs to peer over the grass and make sure it was safe to
cross. Look left, look right, look left again, then cross – but wait
a minute, this chimp has disappeared. It turns out he was scared
of us, for in a minute he reappears a hundred yards farther off,
crossing the road at a steady walk, his head turned to look at us.
In the middle of the road he stops, stands upright for a moment or
two to gaze at us, then goes on to the far side and vanishes into a

little hole in the forest edge. He is following a well-marked chimp track. Now two others cross behind him, a female and an adolescent, then after a moment another female, all looking at us as they go. None makes any sound. We write everything down in the notebook: time of crossing, direction they crossed, sex and age of each individual, special characteristics. Then back to waiting again. Now we hear chorusing distantly in the Siba, whence the chimpanzees we saw just now have come – there are many more left behind; will they follow later? The calling is answered by hoots from the Budongo side, perhaps from our chimps but probably not, as the calls are too far away. Probably the calls came from chimps which crossed earlier in the morning, or perhaps a new group is moving up from deep inside the Budongo, ready to cross back in a few hours time?

During these weeks spent road-watching, we saw hundreds of chimps cross, often the same ones time and time again. As they went they showed themselves to be bold or timid, curious or indifferent, well-built or skinny (none were fat). One mother crossed carrying two babies, the smaller under her belly, the larger on her back, while an even larger third one trailed close behind her. Africans did not seem bothered by the chimps when they met them on the road, nor did the chimps bother about the Africans. It was fascinating to see this crossing of the ways, the road being an artery of communications for humans, driven straight as a die through an arm of inhospitable forest, while for the chimps this red gash of murram was an obstacle to their easy progress through the friendly tangle of greens and browns. Only once did we see chimps make use of the road as humans do; it was the 'royal clan'. The big male appeared first, stepping out on his powerful hands, looking left and right, seeing us, deciding we were harmless, and then beginning to walk *towards* us along the road! As he stepped off, he was followed in single file by the remaining three males in this band – two large and one small. They now ambled along the road towards us, their movements beautifully supple and relaxed, looking around and behind themselves occasionally, but mostly looking at us. Relentlessly the leader male came on; we wondered how close he would come. He paused, and they paused behind him. Then, as if by common agreement, they stepped aside, clambered up the roadside bank and went into their home, the leader stopping awhile in the grass on the bank to study us before he disappeared.

So we passed the days, and they went surprisingly quickly, considering that all we were doing was sitting by the roadside. We plotted calls and crossings on our maps, and built up a fair idea of the distribution of chimpanzees in our immediate area, and every evening we got the reports of our men, so we were able to make quite a wide survey. And though the chimps made it as hard for us as they could, by moving in unpredictable directions (or rather, against our predictions), we began to get some idea of what was going on.

The pattern which emerged was one of chimpanzees concentrated in large numbers in the *Maesopsis* patches, whose location we knew from our Forest Department maps. These *Maesopsis* patches were mostly around the edges of the forest, but sometimes deep inside, and, where the forest was growing rapidly, were sometimes several acres in extent. Within these areas we now, on our trips into the forest, found larger gatherings of chimpanzees than we had hitherto imagined possible, and although we could never see them all we calculated that over fifty animals might be concentrated in an acre of two of *Maesopsis*. Of these, small sub-groups would split off after the morning feed and go roaming, and either we ourselves or our men would frequently see these wanderers, adults mainly, and often just males, crossing tracks on their way to another part of the forest for the day, returning to the *Maesopsis* during the late afternoon for the evening feed. They travelled in groups of half a dozen or so, called often as they went, and doubtless listened carefully to those left behind. Mothers and their 'totos' were rarely to be found in these travelling groups.

And then, inevitably, reported by each of our men in turn, came the phenomenon we had been caught up in ourselves on that day early in the season: the mass movement. First Amis reported it, he had seen *many* chimpanzees ("mingi *mingi*"), thirty or forty of them, they had come thundering up along his valley (which we knew was a traditional chimp route with well-worn tracks) and had made their way northwards with an enormous uproar. We cursed ourselves for not having been there to see and count them, but Amis was clear on one point:

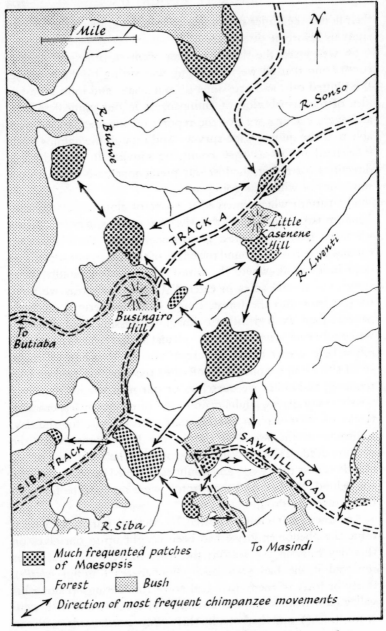

Figure 5. Map showing location of *Maesopsis* trees and
corresponding movements of chimpanzees.

he had seen many mothers and babies with the group. Then Watu Hapana reported the same story, he had counted twenty-three chimpanzees cross the road, making a mark in the ground for each one with his stick; they had all crossed within the space of an hour. We cursed again, but there was no way, short of walkie-talkie, for responding to these situations as they arose.

Not all the chimpanzees were moving around in such large numbers together. One mass movement which we ourselves watched, from the Siba to the Budongo, which followed a stay lasting over a fortnight by large numbers of chimps in a single big *Maesopsis* patch in the Siba, took place in dribs and drabs over two full days. On this occasion seventeen mothers, each with an infant, six childless females, ten young, and thirteen adult males were seen; in addition to these we had probably missed the fore-runners of the move, adult males most likely, since these were already calling ahead when we first arrived to watch. Allowing for these and others we had missed during the two days through not having eyes at the back of our heads, a total of seventy to eighty animals may have crossed.

At the same time we were getting very clear evidence from our co-workers that absolutely no boundaries could be drawn where chimpanzees never crossed from one area into another; small groups were always to be found on the move, crossing every river and track. On the other hand, there were three regions within the study area, each about eight square miles in extent, within each of which chimpanzees were normally to be found, and had been found by us during all the previous months and seasons of our study. We were now able to determine that when a good patch of 'Musisi' was attracting chimpanzees to the Siba, it attracted sixty to eighty animals but did not attract the Kami-rambwa chimps which could be heard by Amis in a Musisi patch at the edge of the forest near the river; and it did not attract the Bubwe River chimps which we knew from Akijero to be feeding on the Musisi patch behind the Game Department huts down below Busingiro. We concluded from this that while each region of six to eight square miles contained sixty to eighty chimpanzees which lived in that region and were able to find within that region a year-round food supply, nevertheless some of these individuals, mainly the adult males and some females, did move freely from one region to another.

As the year had gone by and different species of trees had fruited, different parts of each region had been the focus of the chimpanzees' attention, but we knew each region to contain a sufficiency of every fruit tree utilized by the chimpanzees, and so we had no reason to suppose that the *bulk* of the population of one region would ever leave it and go to another. A simple but very crude analogy can be drawn with humans living in, say, London and Manchester. Each city provides its population with their requirements all the year round, and the bulk of the population is always present in its home city; nevertheless there is continual coming and going between the two. The analogy would be more exact if Londoners, in their search for food, had to spend a month in East Ham (all of them!), a couple of months in Hampstead, a fortnight scattered widely over the whole of the Greater London area, finally converging on, say, Hyde Park for two glorious months, to spread out again along the Edgware Road, Oxford Street, Bayswater Road, and down into Kensington as the pattern of food distribution changed once more, while in Manchester similar events were taking place. But with chimpanzees at ten to the square mile, and city-folk at forty-two to the acre, this analogy should not be taken too seriously.

Getting back to the chimpanzees, we now felt we had the answer to the problem of 'ranges'. Our evidence indicated that such ranges *did* exist for chimps and that, in fact, as far as the chimps were concerned, there is a home-range consisting of an area of some six to eight or more square miles of forest, beyond which the ground is less familiar. Within this home-range live some seventy or so chimpanzees, all of whom, doubtless, know each other (and many of whom must be related to each other). Of these, the aged, the mothers, and the younger children probably do not leave the home-range very often, whereas adult males and some adult females do leave it from time to time and on these occasions, when a number of them meet up with another group, 'carnivals' take place.

Having established the approximate size and number of inhabitants of the ranges, we were in a position to calculate the total chimp population of the forest. In our area they were about ten to the square mile. The Budongo Forest has an area of a hundred and thirty-five square miles, added to which are the thirty-five square miles of the Siba. If the density of chimps in our area was typical, there would be some one thousand seven hundred chimps in the whole forest. But we knew there were vast areas of Ironwood Forest in the north-east of Budongo, and here chimp density would probably be lower. On the other hand, there were some elephant-ridden parts of the Siba where we felt it might be higher. Conclusion: at a safe guess there were between one and two thousand chimpanzees in the forest.

The *Maesopsis* season was glorious and long, it went on all through August and up to mid-September. As it faded and our big clusters of chimpanzees fractured into smaller units, we began to feel that we had accomplished something of what we had set out to do. We had bad days even then, days when not a chimpanzee was heard by any of the men, days when we went in, searching for an elusive band which led us through swamps and even through grassland, tall and dry and ready to burn. But by mid-September we and the men were already talking about "Uhuru" – "Freedom" – Independence Day for Uganda (October 9th) was approaching fast – and about the end of our study, the last pay day, which would follow shortly after. For, despite a generous gift from the Wilkie Foundation of U.S.A. supplementing our University of London grant, we were already running short of money and knew that the next month would have to be our last. We wanted badly to stay a full year, but there just wasn't the money to do it.

And, as if the forest knew our predicament and wanted to comfort us, it began to throw out figs once again on every Mukunyu tree. During our last month, October, there developed a repetition of the scene with which we were so familiar from the February before, of mixed groups of a dozen or so chimpanzees clustered on single ripe fruiting fig trees. It was the start of a new fig season, we were certain of that; figs of all sorts were ripening as well as the Mukunyu. There was the 'Mukunyu Number Two', the 'Mukunyu Number Three', a whole range of 'Nyakatomas' and other figs besides. Time pressed inexorably on and the bank balance dwindled. Our men had to be paid and the bill for the precious knowledge we had gained was cruelly high. Did depression set in? How could it, with Uhuru just a week away?

*

October 9th, 1962: Independence Day for Uganda. We were rounding off our research in the forest, saying good-bye to the trees and tracks and chimpanzees.

During the preceding weeks I had discussed Independence with Manueri and Semei. To Manueri I had jokingly said "On October 9th you will be the 'bwana' and I the servant; you will have to pay me wages", which had tickled him no end. With Semei it was rather different: he took Independence seriously and was genuinely glad to see the white rule go, but he understood that some white men were good for Uganda because they brought her money and trade. He thought, too, that the Uganda Government should now try to loosen the Indian grip on commerce and allow the Africans to take over slowly. Manueri was old and knew things never change; as long as he could work and buy warigi it didn't matter who the Government was. Semei was young and full of ambitions, not only for himself but for his country: maybe he will be a politician one day.

With the Congo so close at hand, and in view of the large number of Congolese immigrants working at the mill and wandering around, we were naturally anxious lest Independence should be an occasion for recriminations against the white community. We had asked Africans what their attitude to us would be after Independence, and they had unanimously expressed the desire to keep us on. They were always courteous and joked with us; and in truth we had no colonialist tradition to embitter them, for Uganda has always been considered a 'black man's land' and colonials going to East Africa have mostly gone to Kenya. Thus very few whites own land in Uganda, most are in Government service, education, or business.

Yet many of the Europeans working at the sawmill had had experience of Mau Mau, and the Congo memory was fresh in our minds. How would the Africans react to 'Uhuru', once their reasoning was befuddled with drink? And drink they would, all

of them were eagerly looking forward to *days*, not hours, at the
pombe barrel. As it happened, we were not the only ones worrying about this problem: so were the local African chiefs. And
they issued a directive to every man in their jurisdiction that if
there was any trouble those responsible would be for it in the
African sense of the word. To make doubly sure they directed
that no Africans were to move around during the drunken days,
Sunday, Monday, and U-day Tuesday. Manueri and Semei told
us they might be late returning for work, since they would be
unable to set out until it was safe for them to walk the roads
again. We gave them some 'Uhuru' meat for the long week-end.

During these Freedom days we Europeans were as home-
bound as the Africans themselves, having no one to look after the
place if we went out, and no great desire to go anywhere. Frankie
and I gazed out over the forest from our verandah; the historic
time arrived and passed by; it rained and the shadows of clouds
passed over the trees. The sun shone again.

In fact the passing of Independence was without incident in
the whole of Uganda. Indeed, except for the celebrations
organized by the various authorities and in a few big commercial undertakings, Independence came as a giant binge, and
passed off as an outsize hangover. We had given our men the
whole of Wednesday off in case the roads were not yet clear,
but midway through the day Manueri returned saying he thought
he'd better get out of it and come back to us or he would die of
liquor. Semei likewise had a tale of much drinking to tell.

The biggest celebrations were in Kampala, where a stadium
had been constructed and a huge crowd watched the tattoo, with
African dancing and highly organized numbers from each part of
the country; in the evening the town went gay. Union Jacks
everywhere came down sedately and were replaced by the new
national emblem: a crested crane in a circle on a striped black,
gold, and red background. Everywhere one sensed the presence
of an ambiguous formality. Was it a hoax? What was freedom?
Would the Baganda now start their tyranny? Would Europeans
leave and jobs be fewer? There was a slogan we often heard:
"Uhuru parmoja" – "freedom together"; I think that most
thinking men in Uganda at that time were a little afraid that in
gaining Independence they would lose those few benefits the

white man had brought: free hospitals, an end to inter-tribal war, some jobs, and a working system of education. In the event nothing changed drastically in our up-country district of Bunyoro and while no Africans suffered from the new regime, we saw few who had benefited. Those few were an extreme minority replacing white men in official positions, a process which had been going on for some time before Independence and continues at the present day.

So Uhuru came to a finish on the Wednesday night and on Thursday we were out again for our last few days of jungle bashing. Time was against us now and yet we could not hurry: it would have spoilt the harmony. The sunrise was the same, and the forest was, and the trees; only we were changing. We said good-bye to it with every step, wondering how life would be without it. For its own part, it was insensitive and innocent, standing silent and raggedly beautiful as we bumped our way out of it for the very last time, bound (how strange it then seemed!) for that distant grey city of the north which claims us as her own.

CHAPTER ELEVEN

The Treatment of Apes in Captivity

In Rosetta Baskerville's book, *The King of the Snakes*,[1] there is a fascinating folk-tale from Uganda called 'The Story of the Fairy Foxes'.

It tells of a king of Uganda who wanted to make a zoo and told his chiefs to bring animals of every kind from the forests and swamps. He put the cages in a beautiful garden and people came from all over the country to see it. The animals were very miserable; night and day they thought of their homes in the forest but no one was sorry for them except the king's dwarf, who had lived in the forest and knew their language. One day when the king was boasting of his fine collection, the dwarf told him there was one animal the zoo lacked: a mysterious creature which was called by some people a 'fairy fox'. The king vowed to go and catch one but, after three months of trying, he was still unsuccessful and when the time came to return home, he was sad.

The dwarf sat near him and said:

' "Why is the king so sad?" And the king answered:

' "I am sorry I have no fairy fox for my Zoo, but there is another reason. I have learnt to love the beautiful forests and jungles and the deep glades and shady paths and water pools, and the moonlight nights are never so lovely in the capital as they are in the country, and I am sad that I must leave it all and return."

'Then the dwarf said: "If you are so sad at leaving the country after only three months, how much more sad must the animals be, for this is their home, and in your wonderful Zoo they are only prisoners."

'When the king heard that he was thoughtful and silent for some time, and then he called Sekibobo and said: "Send a messenger quickly to the capital and tell the Katikiro that all the animals in the zoo are to be sent home, everyone to his own forest or jungle or swamp. I will have no more prisoners." '

[1] *The King of the Snakes*, Rosetta Baskerville, London: Sheldon Press, 1922.

That is an African story; I wish it were an English one too, so that our children could learn it. It might make them a bit more critical in their approach to caged animals.

Three months after returning to England I took my small niece to the zoo. When we came to the chimpanzee cage she said: "Oh look! It's just like a little funny man, isn't it?" "Yes," I said, "just like a little funny man." The chimp suddenly jumped on to a tyre hanging from a rope and swung to and fro, then leaped off the tyre and bounded over to where a bigger, adult chimp was sitting doing nothing in a corner. My niece was delighted. "Isn't he *funny*?" she said. "Yes," I replied.

I didn't mean it, but somehow that wasn't the time and place to say. But now, before this tale which spins around the topic of chimpanzees is told, I want to put down some of my own personal views and those of Frankie, about the keeping of chimpanzees in captivity.

On this subject, Robert Garner can again claim to be a pioneer; the last chapter of his book *Gorillas and Chimpanzees* bears exactly the same title as this chapter. Nearly seventy years have elapsed since he wrote, yet the ideas I shall express will often be the same as his were; unfortunately, the need to express them is even greater today than it was then. Garner saw that the apes he loved must inevitably be captured and caged, and so he pondered on the best way of keeping them. He suggested that they should have a house of their own, eighteen or twenty feet wide by thirty-five or forty feet long, and at least fifteen feet high. The floor should be of earth, with a pool of water twelve or fifteen feet in diameter. The temperature of the building, he said, should be varied from 60° F. to 90° F. From time to time a water spray should be switched on to simulate rain. 'The other end of the building from the pool,' he wrote, 'should be occupied by a strong tree, either dead or alive, to afford the inmates proper exercise.' The south side of the ape-house should be of glass, and so should half the roof, so the sunlight could pour in, and dead leaves should be given to the apes for their comfort. Finally, he suggested, 'another thing which is necessary is to entertain or amuse them in some way, otherwise they become despondent and gloomy. It is believed by those who are familiar with these apes that loneliness or solitude is a fruitful cause of death.'

Thus Garner, in the year 1896. If his ideas had gained currency, many an anthropoid life behind bars would have been saved, and much anthropoid misery could have been avoided. Perhaps because of the expense his ideas would have entailed, Garner had no listeners. Perhaps for the same reason, I shall have none today. But as time passes and the cost of apes steadily rises, reflecting their declining numbers, expensive ape-houses will come to be seen as an investment. Thus, ultimately, the policy of minimising expenditure will have an accidental humanitarian effect. Unfortunately for the chimpanzee, that day will not come until its numbers have been considerably reduced. For the gorilla and orang-utan, however, there are signs that it has already arrived.

I do not want to impute that zoo chiefs and other keepers of apes act purely in accordance with the laws of economics: that would be grossly untrue. At Chester zoo, for example, chimpanzees have not only a big house but a whole paddock to run in, and it is obvious that humanitarian, not financial, considerations have played a big part in arranging the layout of their enclosure. Elsewhere, alas, it is all too often equally clear that the apes have been 'squeezed in'. Here, where top-level planning has gone amiss, a heavy weight of responsibility rests on the keepers to make their animals happy and contented, a job which they often do marvellously despite great odds. But as chimps grow up, their behaviour changes, and very rarely can an adult be satisfied by his keeper, even though the latter may have the best will in the world. And then the misery begins.

Nobody knows how many chimpanzees there are in captivity at the present time, but it runs to several thousands. The market price of a chimpanzee today is from fifty to a hundred and fifty pounds – they are cheap compared with gorillas and orang-utans. No one will ask you what you are going to do with a chimp if you buy one; no one will ask if you know how to keep it, what food to give it; and no one will tell you anything unless you ask. Electrical appliances carry a set of clearly worded 'operating instructions'; not so chimpanzees. If you inquire where the specimen comes from you may be able to discover the name of the dealer's agent but that is about as far as you will get. No details will be available about the manner of its capture, whether the mother was shot or what. You will probably get a youngster as they sell better and are easier to manage, cheaper to house and feed and transport than the bigger ones. Most people, indeed, think of chimpanzees as small animals and are amazed when they hear that a normal adult weighs seven to eight stone. The reason is that it is the youngsters who are on show in tea parties and at circuses and who catch the eye, the older ones having been disposed of or relegated to solitary confinement because – they no longer amuse.

"Off with his head!" said the Queen of Hearts whenever anyone displeased her. In many cases it would be a merciful solution to the problem of what to do with maturing captive chimpanzees. How certain top zoo men can be so heartless always amazes Frankie and me when we see a poor, broken, caged chimp, a big male in the prime of his maturity, gazing out of his lonely little square of space with its hygienic walls and floor, in his eyes a look of resignation that goes sometimes to despair or fury. Such people may be making record profits on their gate receipts, they may be breeding rare species with the utmost care and receiving acclaim from the far corners of the earth, they may have a wider selection of animals than can be seen in any other zoo on earth. In our opinion they lack the one basic quality we expect in any keeper of wild animals, from the child with his pet hedgehog upwards: humanity.

This is neither sentimental nor anthropomorphic. We have spent many days with chimpanzees in their wild state; we have watched them at all ages and at all times of the day, in sunshine and in rain. We never saw a mad chimpanzee, one that sat rocking to and fro, or beating for minutes on end on a log or a branch; the bodies we saw were glossy-haired and the faces alive, the eyes intelligent and sparkling. There were old animals which were skinny and others that were going bald on the head and rump, but there was nothing disconsolate, nothing pathetic about them; they were still very much alive. In due time they would be overcome by physical weakness and so die, but theirs was not the interminable succession of days and nights bounded by the same relentless walls, the same unyielding bars, the same procession of peering faces and bodies of the enemy filing slowly past. If it is possible for a chimpanzee to realize that his whole future will

15*a*. A female and five others feeding in a fig tree.

15*b*. Chimpanzees grooming one another.

16a. When on the move, mothers carry their young.

16b. Mother and baby.

be nothing but this, to relinquish the last flicker of hope for a better life, then such a total misery and frustration must overcome him that I would sooner have him dead. What *hypocrisy* in a people professing a love of animals, and knowing of the remarkable intelligence and emotional make-up of the chimpanzee, to condemn him to life imprisonment with solitary confinement for no fault of his own.

We know the other side of the story by heart, from having heard the arguments so often. Space is expensive or there isn't any; complicated housing is expensive; something is being planned; something will be done soon; labour costs are high; big spaces are unhygienic, cannot be properly cleaned; more keepers and more time would have to be spent and this would be impossible. To all this we respectfully reply that chimpanzees *need* a big space with a variety of objects in it and they *need* the company of others of their kind; if that cannot be provided then they should not be exhibited. There are no half-measures without cruelty; while better accommodation is on the drawing board, let us leave the chimps in the jungle.

> *Stone walls do not a prison make*
> *Nor iron bars a cage . . .*

The poet was, of course, referring to the boundless roaming of the human spirit which cannot be checked by physical barriers. Chimpanzees, alas, have less of this imaginative freedom. Stone walls and bars make very real prisons for them, especially as they grow adult and are less able to make do with the narrow confines and restricted opportunities of their cage, and grow out of playful romping with fellow chimpanzees. It is then that, in the wild, the instinct to wander afar and explore the rich forest environment in their quest for food is growing stronger all the time. In captivity this is when keepers find them getting a bit too strong for comfort, and less reliable at 'tea-parties' and other training routines; the time has come to shut them away like any other dangerous animals. And so their misery begins, *unless* opportunities are provided for the adult activities which are now developing to express themselves.

What these natural adult activities are has not been fully understood until recently. We now know that adult males are

P

extremely mobile, even 'adventurous' in the wild, walking and climbing miles each day. Females and adolescents are mobile too, mothers with their infants less so. Within the context of this pattern of constant movement, the adults perform their other natural behaviour – the drumming, the hooting and hollering, the nest-building, the mating, and so on. But fundamental to any understanding of chimpanzees is the concept of them as *extremely active, adventurous travellers*. In the wild, no chimpanzee could survive for long in one place.

Here, at this fundamental level, is the biggest problem of all which faces zoos, and it is inescapable. Unless the maturing and adult chimpanzee has enough space to do some moving around and exploring, one of its basic instincts will be jammed, and this will affect all of its further behaviour. Space – the one commodity all zoos are shortest of – turns out to be the one essential requirement for the development of natural behaviour in chimpanzees.

Being so arboreal, chimps utilize vertical space as much as horizontal space. The most natural kind of vertical object is, of course, a tree. This provides opportunities for climbing, hanging, swinging, brachiating, and other acrobatics. If the tree has leaves, these provide a measure of security by enabling the animal to hide if it wants to. And at carnival time, a group of chimpanzees needs a tree to stamp, swing, shake, and drum on. Last but not least, a tree will provide the best possible structure for the chimps to nest in, if nesting materials such as loose branches are supplied.

Thus, for a basic chimpanzee enclosure, a paddock or big house or cage with one or more trees in it should be provided. Failing real trees, plastic ones are obtainable on the open market, complete with tough plastic branches and totally inedible hygienic leaves – these plastic trees may be even better than real ones, which the chimps would kill, most probably, by their depredations. In order to provide a drum (plastic or even real trees would not be of much use since they would probably lack the plank buttresses of the forest giants) we suggest a strongly constructed open wooden box, firmly attached to the ground by its smallest side, with six inches between the sounding boards. Other objects in the paddock which provide variety, whatever they are, would be welcome.

In cold countries such as England, an indoor enclosure must

be provided for cold weather. Here the floor will probably have to be of stone, but a cold unyielding floor can be much improved if plenty of straw is provided, to give the animals the comforting feel and smell of organic matter which is their natural home, and even to simulate the bushy depths into which they can so easily and quickly disappear in the forest.

So much for the enclosure. But there is a second set of needs of equal importance which must be met: the *social* needs of chimpanzees. Once again, the most we can hope for is an approximation of conditions in the wild, where over fifty chimpanzees form a kind of population unit whose members meet up from time to time in bands of various sizes. Adult males, we noticed, prefer the company of other adult males; mothers with their infants like to keep together; when a female comes 'on heat' some adult and adolescent males like to follow and mate with her; when there is a common food source all the chimpanzees like to get together. Few zoos will have enough chimpanzees to make these kinds of social grouping a practical possibility, but there is, I think, a fundamental point here about chimpanzees' social needs: they want variety. This is not to say that any two chimpanzees cannot be permanently firm friends – or bitter enemies – every zoo keeper knows they can. Chimps have distinct personalities and, being so similar to humans, these characteristics are easily perceived by us. But, again like ourselves, chimpanzees do like to be able to get away from each other now and then. An adult male doesn't want to be stuck in a cage with one female for years, and if he is he probably will lose interest in her and will not mate with her. But if she is 'somewhere around' – in a nearby cage which he can get into, or in another part of a big enclosure, then he will seek her out when she comes into oestrus and probably mate with her; the rest of the time he can engage in displays and rough-and-tumble activities with other males.

What so often happens in zoos is that a motherless youngster is received. In normal circumstances in the wild, a mother and her offspring stay together for the first five years of its life – a longer period of dependence than in any other primate except man. Even, as is often the case, if the mother has a second baby during this time, both her young stay with her, and we sometimes saw mothers with a big baby riding on the back and a little one under the belly (I once even managed to film this) although the bigger child more often ran on its own. So a pathetic little one- or two-year-old is desperately in need of maternal care. How can zoos provide this? Of course, the favourite mother-substitute is the keeper, who can do a tremendous lot for a baby chimp just by loving it and treating it like a human baby. But even the best zoo keeper has to leave baby alone for long periods, and all of every night. If at all possible, therefore, a baby chimpanzee should be kept with another youngster of about its own age, even if this is not a chimpanzee at all, but, say, a young gorilla or orang-utan. This solution to the problem of the absent mother is scientifically known to assist in normalizing the development of behaviour.

Is it necessary to add that chimpanzees should *never, in any circumstances*, be caged alone? Apart from this being an extreme of heartlessness and cruelty on the part of humans, it can only lead to apathy, depression, neurosis, and psychosis in the ape. Wolfgang Köhler made this point forcibly in 1921, when he wrote: 'It is hardly an exaggeration to say that a chimpanzee kept in solitude is not a real chimpanzee at all.' And he went on to *prove* convincingly that chimpanzees want company: 'It must not be imagined that the isolated ape is sad only because he is in a cage, and the others have more freedom. For if one of them is outside, and the others in the cage, the one outside tries his utmost to get to the others in the cage.' If a prolonged period of isolation is forced on a chimpanzee, most often it is impossible to re-introduce it to others as it has turned 'wild', a thing which is unknown in the wild, the very reverse of normal behaviour.

When the environmental and social needs of chimpanzees have been satisfied, the major problems are overcome. But there remains another set of needs, less tangible but no less real than the first two sets, which have to be satisfied to some extent in order to produce a really lively, happy group. These are the 'motivational' needs. Motivation is the desire, the driving force, which leads all animals including ourselves to do the things we do. In an environment which offers lots of scope for us to do a great variety of things, we are more active because of the continuous motivation to do something than in places where motivation is low. Our motivational needs are our needs to be in places which offer us a variety of things to do. If we are forced into conditions where there is nothing to do, we become desperately eager to escape, and if this is impossible, as in solitary confinement in prisons, we become degenerate and depressive.

In order to provide motivation for captive chimps, one good method, which is fortunately becoming more widespread, is to train them for human entertainment: this gives them something to do, something to look forward to. Frankie and I reject the argument that one should not try to 'turn chimps into human beings'; the whole matter is far more complicated than just this. If dressing them up and giving them tea-pot, cups, and spoons, creates a situation which they enjoy (chimps love hearing applause and human laughter) and shortens their captive day, then let us go on with it and do more of it. Professor Hediger, director of the Zürich zoo, is well known for the emphasis he has always placed on the importance of training captive animals, especially the higher mammals. In 1942 he wrote: 'It is apparent that the lack of anything for the captive animal to do is one of the most pressing problems faced by zoos.' Later, in 1955, he described his reactions to the set-up at the St Louis zoo in America. Here, thirteen chimps had been trained to perform as circus artists, and they gave three shows a day, riding motor cycles and bumper cars, parking themselves in a car park, getting stuck in traffic jams, and even putting themselves into reverse gear if they hit something. 'Personally,' wrote Hediger, 'I first thought this mix-up of creatures from the African virgin forest and modern motor cars somewhat repugnant. When, however, I had seen the whole troupe of chimpanzees waiting, before the curtain rose, for the start of their stage race, I began to see things in a different light.'

But such antics are for chimpanzee youngsters. Adults are less tractable, and their motivational needs are less easy to provide for. The provision of a suitable environment and of company will go a long way in giving adults a variety of things to do. The more complex, or the more varied the enclosure, the happier adults will be in it. There should be blind spots, high spots, things that make noises, things that move, even other species of animals such as monkeys or elephants in with the chimps, as in the Budongo Forest. Our ideal plan for a chimpanzee enclosure would be as follows: several areas are joined by tunnels or ramps, by which chimpanzees can pass from one to another at will. Each area has trees, caves, rocky hills, and a variety of materials for the animals' use, and contains a variety of species as well as the chimpanzees. A moat surrounds the whole enclosure (chimpanzees are afraid of water and unable to swim), and this moat is itself used to house sea-lions and hippos.

We do not imagine that the ideas expressed in this chapter could be put into effect without a long period of careful trial and experiment. But we do believe that *any* steps, however small, in the directions we have indicated, will constitute progress in chimp care. Let us begin, at least, to give our closest relative in the animal kingdom a square deal. The rewards could be great, for the increased mental well-being of the chimpanzees in our zoos will ensure that they will live longer, healthier lives, and that they will breed at a rate approaching the situation in the wild, where a female has a new baby every three years or so. At the moment, not a single zoo can boast of such a record, and many have never had a chimpanzee birth at all.

Certain zoos, a good example being Chester, have already put many of the ideas expressed above into practice: we commend their efforts heartily. Others have not made a start. In the past they have been able to claim lack of knowledge to cover up their lack of humanity; now this course is debarred to them. If they do not act, I hope public indignation will stir them to do something. England is world-famous for her general humanitarian approach to animals, but her zoos do not all justify the claim. Let us start now, where a start is most needed, with better conditions for chimpanzees.

Addendum to Chapter Eleven

This chapter describes the situation as it was on our return from Uganda. Since then the Animals (Restriction of Importation) Act 1964 has been passed, and this goes some way towards preventing the imperfections pointed out. For example the importation of apes by private persons will be prohibited, and zoos will have to have breeding colonies before being licensed to buy apes.

Further Reading

Garner, R. L. *Gorillas and Chimpanzees*. Osgood, McIlvaine & Co., London, 1896.

Harrison, B. *Orang-utan*. Collins, London, 1962.

Schaller, G. B. *The Year of the Gorilla*. Collins, London, 1965.

Stanley, H. M. *The Great Forest of Central Africa: its cannibals and pigmies*. Printed for the author, London, 1890.

Yerkes, R. and Yerkes A. *The Great Apes*. Yale University Press, 1929.

Other Books mentioned in the text

Baskerville, R. *The King of the Snakes*. Sheldon Press, London, 1922.

Battell A. Quoted in Purchas S., *Hakluytus Posthumous, or Purchas his Pilgrimes*, 4th edition, vol. 2., W. Stansby, for H. Fetherstone, London, 1626.

Beattie, John. *Bunyoro*. Henry Holt, New York, 1960.

Burroughs, E. R. *Tarzan of the Apes*. Methuen, London, 1916.

Churchill, W. S. *My African Journey*. Neville Spearman and Holland Press, London, 1908, 1962.

Du Chaillu, P. *Explorations and Adventures in Equatorial Africa*. John Murray, London, 1861.

Eggeling, W. J. 'Observations on the Ecology of the Budongo Rain Forest, Uganda', *Journal of Ecology*, pp. 20–87, 1947.

Fabre, J. H. *Souvenirs Entomologiques*, Vol. 1, Librairie Ch. Delagrave, Paris, 1897.

Hediger, H. *Studies of the Psychology and Behaviour of Captive Animals*. Butterworth, London, 1955.

Johnston, H. *The Uganda Protectorate*. Hutchinson, London, 1902.

Köhler, W. (English edition 1957). *The Mentality of Apes*. Penguin Books, Middx, 1957 (originally 1925).

Kortlandt, A. 'Chimpanzees in the Wild'. *Scientific American*, May, 1962.

Livingstone, D. *The Last Journals of David Livingstone in Central Africa*. John Murray, London, 1874.

Moorehead, A. *No Room in the Ark*. Hamish Hamilton, London, 1959.

Nissen, H. W. 'A Field Study of the Chimpanzee'. *Comparative Psychology Monographs*, vol. 8, pp. 1–22, 1931.

List of Latin Names
of Species Referred to in the Text

adder, night	*Causus rhombeatus*
ant, safari	*Dorylus* sp.
baboon	*Papio anubis*
bamboo	*Arundinaria alpina*
banana, wild	*Musa* sp.
barkcloth tree	*Ficus natalensis*
bat, fruit	*Pteropodidae*
beetle, black dung	*Carabidae*
goliath	*Goliathus goliathus*
metallic green dung (jewel)	*Buprestidae*
boomslang, green	*Dispholidus typus*
buffalo, black	*Cyncerus caffer*
red Congo	*Cyncerus nanus*
bushbaby	*Galago demidoffi*
bushbuck	*Tragelaphus scriptus*
butterfly, crimson-winged	*Cymothoe* sp.
indigo-winged	*Precis* sp.
swallowtail	*Papilionidae*
chimpanzee	*Pan troglodytes schweinfurthii*
cicada	*Cicadidae* probably *Platypleurinae*
civet	*Viverra civetta*
cobra, black-lipped	*Naja melanoleuca*
cork tree	*Erythrina* sp.
cormorant	*Phalacrocorax* sp.
crane, crowned	*Balearica regulorum*
dove, blue-spotted wood	*Turtur afer*
duiker, blue	*Cephalophus monticolus*
red	*Cephalophus natalensis*
eagle, fish	*Cuncuma vocifer*
egret, yellow-billed	*Mesophoyx intermedius*
elephant	*Loxodonta africana*
everlasting flowers	*Helichrysum nandense*
firefly	*Telephoridae*
fly, buttress	*Trentopohlia* sp.
elephant	*Tabanus xanthomelas*
lantern	*Zanna tenebrosa*
red-eyed (Congo floor maggot)	*Auchmeromyia luteola*
fly-catcher, black	*Melaenornis edolioides*
francolin	*Francolinus* sp.
francolin, Nahan's forest	*Francolinus nahani*

frog, tree	*Hyperolius* sp.
gorilla	*Gorilla gorilla beringei*
guinea-fowl, crested	*Guttera edouardi*
tufted	*Numida meleagris*
hawk-eagle, long-crested	*Lophoaëtus occipitalis*
heather, giant	*Erica arborea* or *Philippia johnstonii*
heron	*Ardea* sp.
hippopotamus	*Hippopotamus amphibius*
hog, red river	*Potamochoerus porcus*
wart	*Phacochoerus aethiopicus*
hornbill, black-and-white casqued	*Bycanistes subcylindricus*
white thighed	*Bycanistes albotibialis*
horsefly	*Tabanus besti*
hyrax, tree	*Dendrohyrax arboreus*
'Igeria' tree	*Pseudospondias microcarpa*
Ironwood tree	*Cynometra alexandri*
kingfisher, pied	*Ceryle rudis*
kob, Uganda	*Kobus thomasi*
leopard	*Panthera pardus*
lichen	*Usnea* sp.
lion	*Panthera leo*
mahogany trees	*Khaya anthotheca Entandrophragma utile, E. angolense, E. cylindricum.*
mamba	*Dendroaspis* sp.
mantis	*Mantis religiosa*
marabou stork	*Leptoptilos crumeniferus*
mongoose	
monkey, black-and-white colobus	*Colobus abyssinicus*
blue	*Cercopithecus mitis stuhlmanni*
golden	*Cercopithecus mitis kandti*
redtail	*Cercopithecus ascanius*
vervet	*Cercopithecus aethiops*
moth, Emperor	*Saturnidae*
'Mpungu' tree	*Chrysophyllum perpulchrum*
'Mujgangoma' tree	*Cordia millenii*
'Mukunyu' trees	*Ficus mucuso, F. capensis, F. sycomorus*
'Mumule' tree	*Holoptelea grandis*
'Munyama' tree	*Khaya anthotheca*
'Muvule' tree	*Chlorophora excelsa*
'Muyati' tree	*Mildbraediodendron excelsum*
'Ngrube' tree	*Melanodiscus* sp. *nov.*
'Nyakatoma' trees	*Morus lactea, Ficus natalensis,* and other *Ficus* spp.
pangolin	*Manis tricuspis*
parrot, grey	*Psittacus erithacus*
pelican	*Pelecanus* sp.
pig, bush	*Potamochoerus porcus*
porcupine	*Hystrix africae-australis*
potto	*Periodicticus potto*

python	*Python sebae*
rat, edible	*Thryonomys swinderianus*
rattan	*Calamus* sp.
robin-chat, white-browed	*Cossypha heuglini*
roller, blue-throated	*Eurystomus gularis*
broad-billed	*Eurystomus glaucurus*
shrew, elephant	*Rhynchocyon cirnei*
snail-slug	*Testicella* sp.
snake, olive house	*Boaedon lineatum*
starling, purple-headed glossy	*Lamprocolius purpureiceps*
stick insect	*Phasmidae*
termite, rustling	*Macrotermitinae*
savanna	*Macrotermes bellicosus*
tortoise, land	*Kinixys* sp.
turaco, black-billed	*Tauraco schütii*
viper, Gaboon	*Bitis gabonicus*
waterbuck	*Kobus defassa*
yellow-bill	*Ceuthmochares aereus*

General Index